Not another care handbook

Pearls of wisdom for care managers

HAWKER PUBLICATIONS

Not Another Care Handbook:
Pearls of wisdom for care managers

First published in 2014 by

Hawker Publications Ltd, Culvert House, Culvert Road, London SW11 5DH

Tel: 020 7720 2108
Website: www.careinfo.org

Copy editors: Kate Hawkins, Fiona Robb
Project management and editing: Geoff Hodgson
Book design by Prepare to Publish Ltd, mail@preparetopublish.com
Printed and bound in Great Britain by Truprint Media, Margate

British Library Cataloguing in Publication Data
A catalogue record for this book is available from the British Library

ISBN 978 1 874790 93 8

Hawker Publications publishes a range of books for the health and social care sectors.
For more information: www.careinfo.org

Hawker Publications also publishes *Caring Times* and the *Journal of Dementia Care*.

Dedicated to

The care worker we would all like looking after us:

My dear wife
Dr Jane Foley MBBS FRCP

Acknowledgements

I would like to express my gratitude and thanks to a lot of people who helped with the concept of *Not another care handbook: Pearls of wisdom for care managers*. First, of course, I would like to thank the 106 authors who contributed such wisdom and experience within their chapters. Next I would like to thank Craig Woollam of Savills, Peter Grose of Lester Aldridge and Chris Manthorp, consultant and writer, for their wise guidance and enthusiasm for the idea of bringing together large numbers of experienced care workers at all levels and getting them to write about their passion: care. I would also like to thank Rev Dr Keith Albans of Methodist Homes for his superb marshalling of the end of life care section and Paul Ridout of Ridouts LLP for persuading so many of his colleagues to write for the legal quagmires and pitfalls section.

Asking 106 people to write a chapter each is no mean task so it was essential that the idea was attractive to authors, that they would deliver and the appropriate logistics were in place to make the publishing process acceptable to everyone. Multi-author books are common but the sheer number of authors for *Not another care handbook: Pearls of wisdom for care managers* has made it unique! For all to happen so successfully I am greatly indebted to two consummate professionals – Andrew Chapman of Prepare to Publish and our own Geoff Hodgson of Caring Times. I won't say there wasn't the odd glitch but, given the complexity of the task, working with all the authors to publish *Not another care handbook* has proved a real pleasure.

Foreword

BARBARA POINTON MBE

Former carer, Ambassador for the Alzheimer's Society and Dementia UK

What a remarkable handbook this is. Intended for managers of care homes, when you open it, you have at your fingertips more than a hundred experienced professionals who work in different roles in care homes, each eager to share with you their personal pearls of wisdom. They speak with honesty and passion about their particular role and what makes for excellent care and support for all residents, including the large number who have dementia. Through 10 key points, each person passes on helpful practical tips, sound advice and frequently an insight into what makes them tick.

Placed firmly at the core of their thinking and actions is the wellbeing of the resident. By discovering what is important to each individual, their background and personal preferences (including emotional and spiritual needs), they demonstrate how they nurture the whole person. Not forgetting environment, access to fresh air, plentiful activity (whether solitary or in groups) and the therapeutic effect of creativity, fun and laughter.

As the manager, you set the tone and ethos and lead by example from the front, but you also have a business to run. Responsibilities can weigh heavily, so help is at hand from contributors advising on finance, inspections, marketing, legal pitfalls and managing risk versus benefit. Your most valuable resource lies in working with the staff as a team, so advice is offered for recruitment, motivation, training, retention and mutual support.

By ensuring that staff bring understanding, competence and compassion to the job and can form friendly relationships with the resident and their relative or friend, that important triangle of mutual trust and communication is created, which immediately enhances care. Both staff and family appreciate emotional support when the going gets tough, especially at end of life.

I found it a privilege to reach out and catch these pearls of wisdom; the insights gained will inspire both you and your staff, resulting in personal job satisfaction, residents who feel cherished, peace of mind for families and warm appreciation from your community.

Introduction

DR RICHARD HAWKINS

trained as a doctor and worked as a surgeon for the NHS and then part-time for the charity Marie Stopes. In 1985 he co-founded Hawker Publications, a publisher with a particular interest in social care and dementia, and the publisher of Caring Times and the Journal of Dementia Care

There comes a time in any community's life when some of the leaders within it have been learning, sharing and providing good practice for long enough to become experts. That collective wisdom is a precious resource and needs to be captured and offered to the community and to a wider audience.

Not another care handbook: Pearls of wisdom for care managers is an attempt to capture the now considerable collective wisdom within the care home sector, and to provide it in a succinct style which appeals to modern readers, using both printed and electronic formats.

Not another care handbook is not a reference tome or textbook; it makes no attempt to cover topics methodically. Its driving force is offering ideas to the manager. We hope that the experience of reading *Not another care handbook* will be like attending an excellent conference, where every chapter mirrors the experience of meeting leading figures in the sector over coffee and picking up unique and invaluable pearls of wisdom.

People have asked me whether there are any themes which emerge from all the chapters. There is one powerful one. It is that everyone believes the quality of care transcends all other considerations within the (now many) walls of the care home. Among the 106 authors there are representatives from the different professions who play key roles in the modern care home and each one of them keeps returning to the central theme that everything flows from the provision of the highest quality care for the residents. This focus on quality reflects my personal experience of the sector but it is gratifying nevertheless to find it so clearly described within these pages. *Not another care home* makes a strong case for the continuing importance of the role of the care home as part of modern healthcare and social care – and by extension for the key role of the manager within it.

Not another care handbook

Pearls of wisdom for care managers

1. Learning from each other

2. What's it like being...

3. Key management topics

4. Promoting your home successfully

5. Legal quagmires and pitfalls

6. Running a safe home

7. Staff: Your most valuable resource

8. Getting personal

9. Valuing and working with residents / family / friends

10. Activities

11. Special challenges

12. End of life care

13. Reflections

1

Learning from each other

Quality care and why it is so important

Mike Parsons *is founder and chief executive of multiple-award winning Barchester Healthcare. He started the company following a successful career in advertising and marketing.*

Quality is the issue that bought me into care management. I found myself helping my mother look for a care home for my two great aunts. I was appalled by the dreadful quality of the nursing and residential homes I visited. My mother's aunts were people with plenty of life about them. It was immediately clear to me that they deserved better than the poor excuses for care that were on offer. I decided to start a home based on hospitality, enjoyment of life and the highest quality services. Barchester Healthcare began at that moment.

People deserve quality

Quality is important because the people we look after deserve the best we can give them. People who have worked all their lives and are now vulnerable and in need of help should be given the best environment, hospitality and care that we can provide. That's the baseline.

A positive experience

People usually come into care because they have few other options. It's a distress purchase, often made under considerable pressure. Proving a genuinely high quality service can transform the decision into a positive experience.

Enjoying life

High quality homes offer people the opportunity to enjoy their lives. Homes must offer good, professional clinical care but they must also allow people to carry on doing the activities that they most enjoy, from cooking to golf or theatre visits, from looking after pets to spending time with a good book. If they need help to achieve what they once managed for themselves, homes should offer it as unobtrusively as possible.

Taking pride in what we do

Staff work more creatively and enjoy their work more in an environment where they know they are offering people the best they can. It's vital to be able to take pride in your work. That's at the core of high quality care.

Quality makes financial sense

People will recognise and pay for quality. That's why Barchester has grown so rapidly, from the initial base of Moreton Hill – all I had in mind at the start – to more thanr 200 homes and rising.

A sense of purpose

The quality of our care homes gives me a purpose and a pride in my work, which is very important to me.

Keeping the commitment

It is always an interesting struggle to maintain high levels of quality. Barchester has won awards for everything from building design to training, and many individual awards, which provides objective backing for our approach, but it needs to be constantly refreshed. The key is good, career enhancing training and employing the right people. We link that with well designed environments and work on a thorough understanding at all levels of the company of our commitment to hospitality and high quality services.

"Raise your quality standards as high as you can live with, avoid wasting your time on routine problems and always work as closely as possible to the boundary of your abilities. Do this because it is the only way of discovering how that boundary moves forward."

– EDSGER W DIJKSTRA

Quality must be worked at

Quality is not something that can be taken for granted. It involves constant growth and evolution, learning from success and failures, and it's what makes running Barchester so interesting.

Something to aspire to

We have worked hard to ensure that Barchester homes are at the forefront of high quality care, and aim to raise standards across the sector as a whole. People can see what's possible, and have something to aspire to. That's a source of pride.

Future challenge

The future of care homes will be very different. Base line quality issues will remain but high quality care homes will be open community resources, much more involved with local life. That's a revolutionary prospect.

What working for more than 20 years in long term care has taught me

MAHESH PATEL

is a serial entrepreneur and currently chief executive of Minster Care Group.

He previously established and successfully exited care groups Highclear, Kingsclear & ILG and also investments in children's nurseries, prosthetics and factoring.

After 25 years working in care, I know that the position of care home manager is tough but it is also incredibly rewarding. You are the most important people in the sector because success or failure depends, to a large extent, on you – and your team of course. If you don't want that kind of responsibility, don't become a manager! There will be all sorts of financial pressure put on you, but if you treat your residents with respect, value their dignity and provide outstanding care, everything else will flow from there.

Use your clients' eyes

Always look at your home through the eyes of prospective residents/relatives. They may have a perspective which is rather different to yours – they may focus on 'small' matters such as the quality of the decorating, smells, first impressions of the home which may be far removed from your "grand" focus on care planning, CQC visits and staff training.

Keep it simple

First impressions of your home are very important. Make sure they work for you. Simple things can make a big difference. For example, I always watch carefully how staff address residents, relatives, other staff, and visitors providing a service to the home.

You're in charge!

Make sure everyone knows who's in charge of your home. In the past matrons wore a splendid hat for a very good reason - no one could fail to know who the boss was! I personally like uniforms –especially in nursing homes, because everyone knows who's who. If you are weak, people will take advantage of you – nowhere is this better illustrated than with CQC inspections. Inspectors have an uncanny ability to spot a weak manager, and in no time they will be playing on this and pushing you into places you shouldn't be and won't like.

Relatives will be your friends

Proactively involve relatives in your planning and in all aspects of your home. When they first start visiting a home they have a tendency to be hypercritical but it is amazing how quickly they will come round to your side if you involve them in decision-making. Another winner with relatives is to always offer them food at mealtimes, the extra cost is negligible but you will have gained invaluable ambassadors for your home.

Success or failure? – it depends on you

Let's not mince words – if you are the manager of a care home for any length of time, ultimately its financial success will depend on you. Successful marketing is the key. Placing ads in the local paper can be less productive. Instead you must focus on making your home the centre of the local community by thoughtful planning and by using your imagination. We find, for example, that inviting local associations and clubs to use our public rooms in the evening is a very successful way to get influential local people on-side and away from the old "them and us" attitudes of the past.

Mentors are great

Everyone needs help and support at times. Regional managers and owners want to help (usually!) but they are still your line manager. We find the "buddy system" works really well, especially for new managers. Having a manager from another care home, at the same level as you, to ring for advice or a moan, or to meet you for a coffee, is just what you need.

"Always bear in mind that your own resolution to succeed is more important than any other one thing."

– Abraham Lincoln

What's the local competition up to?

Find out about the local competition. Supermarkets and hotels do it all the time with success, and you should too.

What's really happening in your home?

Talk to your residents about what is happening day in and day out at your home. Many of them have a wealth of experience and can give you excellent feedback on what is *really* happening in your home, especially when you are not there.

Be prepared to say no

Don't just take every possible resident in an effort to fill a new home quickly or keep an older one full. Take time and care with your assessments because some residents simply won't fit in and the challenges they present will lose you more than you gain.

A hundred small disasters add up to a big disaster

It's easy to ignore small things – a messy flowerbed in the front garden, a missing tile, a dripping tap, cracked plates, a scuffed corridor – because individually they may not seem important but add them all up together and they become huge. So, do the rounds with your maintenance staff and get the small things sorted – you'll find it makes getting the big things right much easier.

What I want to find when visiting a care home

CRAIG WOOLLAM

is head of healthcare at Savills. Craig joined Savills in 1999 to create the Healthcare division. Prior to that, he spent 16 years at Christie & Co where he was a main board Director and their head of corporate healthcare.

When I first started work in the care sector as a fresh faced business agent in 1986 the market was a very different place. We had few corporate operators, the average care home was under 25 beds, shared rooms and wards were the norm, purpose built homes were a rarity and we had limited regulation. Over the years I have witnessed a marked change in physical standards. However, most of the fundamentals that I look for have not changed that much.

My prime focus is the valuation and sale of registered care homes as trading entities and thus I am looking at the sector as an external advisor rather than from an internal operations perspective. However, with the sheer volume of homes that both I and my team at Savills inspect, I like to believe we know what we are looking for.

External appearance

First for me is external appearance. Poorly maintained gardens, peeling external paintwork and plant life in gutters as a first impression are very off-putting.

Parking

Is parking adequate? In some central urban locations this can be a challenge but if parking is limited is there a drop off point by the main entrance with level access to the accommodation.

Friendly welcome

I look for a friendly and positive welcome. Is the visitor left waiting for ages having rung the door bell? Who greets you at the door and are you asked to sign in on arrival (often a good sign). Does the property feel like a home or an institution? I like to see a clean, bright and welcoming entrance area with certificates and home information clearly displayed.

Seeing, hearing and smelling

Once in the building my eyes, ears and sense of smell are key.

State of repair

As I move around the accommodation I will look for broken, damaged or frayed furnishings, carpets or curtains. Is there evidence of ongoing repairs and maintenance?

Resident bedrooms

Do the bedrooms have residents' names on the door? If a bedroom is empty and say the resident is at lunch or in the lounge area, is the bed made, are the curtains open and is the room generally tidy?

Housekeeping

Are there sufficient storage areas? Is the kitchen adequately ventilated and well positioned for deliveries and is the laundry clean and tidy ?

Staff impressions

When we value a business we will inspect the key parts of the accommodation and hold discussions with either the proprietor or manager. A good sign for me is a manager or proprietor who knows the names of the residents and staff, who is on duty that day, which residents are in their rooms, etc. Are the staff visibly spending time interacting with residents rather than huddled around the office or staff room? Does the cook vary the menu and is help given with feeding for more dependent residents ? Other pointers that I look for are: Is the staff team settled and staff turnover low? Is agency staff usage at a realistic level? Does the home have a good deputy manager and administrator who know how the home functions? Is the office tidy and organised? Is there evidence of ongoing and up to date staff training?

"During the past 27 years I have visited well over 1,000 care homes of varying size, registration and quality. A number of the homes have been inspirational, many excellent and sadly some have been very poor indeed. A basic key question that I still ask myself is: Would I be happy to see my mother or father living in this home?"

Activities

Are the residents warehoused in one area e.g. chairs arranged around the walls of a lounge with a loud television on but no one watching it? I like to see multiple and occupied day and quiet areas in a home. What does the activities schedule look like?

Quality of care

Ultimately it is the quality of care, systems and operations in this business which are absolutely key, and to a large extent outweigh physical standards.

What running a domiciliary care company has taught me

SUSHIL RADIA

has 25 years sector experience at Care First Care Homes (Bupa Care Homes) and Westminster Homecare Ltd, as chairman of Counsel & Care (now part of Independent Age) and Trustee of RMBI & Centre for Policy on Ageing.

Domiciliary care is a people business. I have learnt that with planning, organisation, and training, a high quality, safe, personalised and appropriate service can be delivered in the home. Commissioners play a key role but it requires an empathetic staff group to deliver this vital support.

Part of the continuum of care

Putting the older individual at the centre and with a proper direction of resources, a preventative and enabling service can lead to fulfilling lives based on choice, independence, and dignity. Homecare, residential care and hospital care are not mutually exclusive but can and should work together and society as a whole should take responsibility.

Staff quality and logistics are key

Organising delivery of domiciliary care is a logistics exercise, but not a parcel delivery service. With sophisticated systems and modern technology, a service can be provided that matches individual needs with compatible care workers, deals with and records changes as they happen. However the service is only as good as the staff.

Robust recruitment and skilled management

A unique feature of homecare is that the staff work independently in the community looking after dependent clients, without any direct supervision. This requires robust recruitment procedures and a skilled management team that has an understanding of basic care principles, legislation and is supportive of the field staff. It has been said that "people work for people" and not for organisations. Nowhere is that more true than a homecare business.

People must be allowed to decide what's best for them

In homecare, as in care homes, purchasing decisions seem to be overriding commissioning. The commissioners (including families) must let the individual decide what is good for them, giving them the opportunity to design their care and support plan with the provider. However service expectations have not been supported with funding, resulting in disappointments, service curtailments and occasional failures.

Regulator should take a lead role

The regulatory framework is only ten years old and is now becoming sector-specific, evolving with the increasing importance of homecare, and moving from a critical albeit reactive role to the direction of service and quality of services. In my view, the regulator can and should shape, lead and be a 'champion', and not just a referee between the competing stakeholders.

Advanced training and technology

Homecare now encompasses the full range of services from basic practical support, through to medication administration, dementia care and end of life care. Homecare staff undertake tasks that previously were the preserve of qualified medical staff or required staying in a care facility. This has been achieved by considerable investment in training and this transfer will continue as we acquire more skills and implement advanced telecare.

Learning from customer feedback

Homecare is about caring for vulnerable individuals in their homes. We all know what good care is and when it is properly done or badly delivered. We learn a lot from the complaints and the compliments that we receive. What we need to do is maintain consistency and continuity, which can be achieved by focusing on the service user, use of technology and judicious deployment of staff in an increasingly ageing society.

"As time goes my mother's health declines and needs become more problematic. However, with people like 'X' in your employ it allows people like my mother to remain in their own homes for as long as possible."

– Mrs E.F., a service user's daughter 28th June, 2013

Resources directed at front-end services

Homecare as a business proposition is a small ticket item operation, paid and charged in units of 15 minutes, with some authorities now paying only for contact time. It therefore requires micro-managing and attention to detail, in the back office and support services, with rigorous control on costs and resources directed at front-end services. Once again it is the commissioners/purchasers who are determining the outcomes.

Stakeholders' interests must be aligned

Good care is good business. In the UK social care is provided mainly by the private sector, which occasionally (and justifiably) gets a bad name when there is service failure with the assumption it's the profiteering, but gets no credit for the successes. In my view the failures, public or private sector, are due to poor management and conflicting targets. The interests of all the stakeholders must be aligned, including the entrepreneurs being recognised for their skills and contribution.

A sustainable model needs adequate funding

Finally a good sustainable model that provides support to our ageing population will require appropriate funding and an integrated care service that, I believe, should be user-led and directed.

View from the top

MIKE PARISH

has been chief executive of Care UK since 2001, Mike was previously on the board of global supply chain solutions provider Exel PLC.

Local authorities are in a funding crisis, and the NHS must change from its predominantly hospital-based model of care. Long-established organisations tend to focus inwardly and create boundaries that their customers are expected to navigate. In our world this is exemplified by the Berlin Wall between social care and the NHS, by the separation between community and residential social care, and primary and secondary health care. One thing I've learnt in my career is that necessary change often requires a burning platform. Here are some other things I've learnt. I hope you find them useful.

Put the customer first

Always put the customer first. It's that simple. Take responsibility for the care you provide and the person in your care. Your obligation to them trumps any you have to colleagues or your organisation. That also means you have a duty to raise issues and concerns.

Good leadership is crucial

There's a direct correlation between the calibre of a service manager and the quality of care their service provides. A care manager must have a breadth of capabilities: be highly empathetic to customers' needs, and those of relatives, staff and commissioners; they must be clinically able, have organisational management ability and commercial acumen.

High quality care is all that matters

You can only provide the best care if everyone in your team is engaged and motivated, and it's the manager's priority to make this happen. Having half your team engaged isn't enough. Having beautiful surroundings isn't enough. You need everyone committed to doing the best for customers.

Stand your ground

We sometimes have to make difficult value judgements. If you're asked to deliver care that you know won't meet a person's needs, push back. You can refuse to take on work, or a new resident. Where you can, work with commissioners to deliver appropriate, cost effective care.

Keep calm and find out more

When you hear a worrying complaint or a bad news story about to break, take a calm, considered approach and establish the facts. You're often dealing with differing perspectives, emotion and, sometimes, family dynamics. There are often two sides to a story.

There's no excuse for inefficiency

In our sector it has become vital to be able to deliver high quality care at a price that the customer can pay. Good information management systems will help you to create efficiency, and therefore quality. They'll highlight what's going well and what isn't, so you can immediately fix the issues.

Get comfortable with change

Change is a constant: society changes, customers' needs change. Care plans, carers and homes must adapt. Successful care organisations understand change and adapt to it – the really good ones help drive it. However, ensuring continuity of care is a must. Older people get very unsettled seeing a different carer every day.

Hobby horse

How often do care providers abandon a customer when they become challenging – maybe dumping a resident at A&E because of their challenging behaviour? Whose interests come first: the organisation's or the customer's? The response from providers is invariably, "We're not like that". But is that really true?

Be an all-round care expert

The coming years will see huge growth in the number of people aged over 85, coinciding with self-funding becoming the norm. As well as being an expert in care, you must be an expert in funding and navigating the system. There's a lot of confusion and misinformation out there!

Become a personal advocate

See yourself as a personal advocate for current or prospective customers and their families. Offer them advice and support as they grapple with their challenges. It's often a hugely stressful time for them, and your experience, knowledge, support and understanding can make a big difference.

Empowering independence

Help people to live in their own homes for as long as possible to maintain their independence and wellbeing. Help people with mental health issues to recover, or those with physical disabilities to live normal lives. In a care home, avoid treating residents as if they've lost all capability – enable and stimulate them.

What working in the learning disability world has taught me

NEIL MATTHEWMAN

is chief executive of Community Integrated Care, a national health and social care charity that supports thousands of people living across England and Scotland with learning disabilities, mental health concerns, autism and age-related needs.

Leading Community Integrated Care has taught me a great deal about the care sector, the incredibly dedicated people who work within it and the amazing lives that people with support needs can lead. It gives me tremendous pleasure to be able to share with you some of the insight that I have gained throughout a career of working with – and for – people with learning disabilities.

See the individual

People with learning disabilities should be valued as the individuals they are – not treated as though they are part of a collective. It is vital that care services recognise this individuality and understand their role in supporting people to achieve their fullest personal potential.

One size *doesn't* fit all

Fundamentally, a 'one size fits all' approach to delivering care and support is wrong. As a sector, we must never revert to delivering institutional practice – ignoring or overriding the voice of the people who we are entrusted with caring for. Support should be tailored to each individual – built on an understanding of their life history, personality and aspirations.

Give just enough support

Care providers must avoid becoming too 'paternalistic' – over-supporting people to the point that, without realising, they have constrained independence or stymied life-experience. We should support people with learning disabilities to *do* things – not just do things *for* people with learning disabilities.

Focus on outcomes

All services should be focused on enabling the people they support to achieve great outcomes – both in their everyday life as well as in their longer-term aspirations. Having a learning disability should not be a barrier to living a life that is filled with purpose, friendships and a sense of belonging.

Environments matter

I have seen first-hand, throughout my career, the amazing impact that the right living environment can make to people with learning disabilities. Staff working in care services should always ask themselves: "Would I be happy for myself, or one of my loved ones, to live here?" If the honest answer is 'no', then you've got to put things right.

Relationships are vital

At the core of great care are great relationships: between the person who receives support, their loved ones and the carers who support them, as well as between the care provider and its professional partners. Positive relationships are founded upon respect and a common understanding, and require effort to be nurtured and maintained.

Perfect partnerships

It is important to work with the right people when developing services. This should begin with your most important customers – the people you support and their loved ones. But also be receptive to outside insight too; listen to the experience of your professional partners – be they GPs or social workers, commissioners or housing associations.

Learn from others

The very best care services, I find, have a culture of learning and looking outwards at the good work of others. Seek out examples of best practice through training or independent research, attend conferences or local forums, and ask questions of senior people in your own organisation. Be ambitious in your learning and strive to apply the knowledge you gain in your own service.

"Never lose sight of the fact that the most important yardstick of your success will be how you treat other people – your family, friends, and co-workers, and even strangers you meet along the way."

– Barbara Bush, wife of the 41st President of the United States, George Bush Sr.

Value your staff

Our staff often take for granted the fantastic outcomes that they help people to achieve, simply believing that their dedication and ambition is just part of their 'day job'. Great care should not be taken for granted – it takes skill, commitment, and patience, and we should do more to recognise this. Commend good work and never let the exceptional go unnoticed.

Remember: you make a difference!

There is no greater satisfaction than knowing that your work helps someone to live a better life and fulfil their greatest potential. While working in care undoubtedly comes with significant responsibility and frequently brings difficult challenges, we must never lose sight of our privileged roles. Your job makes a difference – remember that when the times get tough.

Reflections of a care provider

MIKE ROYCROFT

recently retired as chief executive of the Whiteley Homes Trust. He was previously director of primary healthcare for the Army in UK.

Mike Rowcroft reflects on more than nine years as "Warden of Whiteley Village" and some seven years as Chairman of the Surrey Care Association. Whiteley Village has been providing housing, support and care to some 500 elderly residents for nearly a century. It is now exceptional in providing the whole spectrum from retirement/supported living, through extra-care to residential, nursing and palliative care. He feels that, although perhaps they are 'givens' or obvious to those with experience of working with older people, there are some key messages he would pass on:

Life skills

People are not born old – they acquire a wealth of experience and skills and even when their faculties start to fade, they want and can contribute to society whether that is wider society or their local community. Providers must facilitate what people can do rather than being limited by what they cannot.

Meeting and managing expectations

The expectations of the 'new Old', today's and tomorrow's older people (and their relatives) are, quite rightly, different to those of the 'old Old'. Providers must actively make themselves aware of those expectations and remain open to new ideas but also ensure that good communication helps the older people's expectations to be managed when they cannot be met.

Residential care is valuable

The "Care Home bad - everything else good" view of many care commissioners must be challenged. Residential care is important and in the best interests of many individuals, and not just a last resort. Even in a care village where every service is available so that individuals can receive domiciliary (even palliative) care in their dwelling, there is still a need for residential care when their needs become too great or when they want it (for company, for example).

Risk taking

Even though it is difficult in these litigious days, providers must have the courage to strike the balance between avoiding risk and facilitating self-determination. Adults, even if seen by others as vulnerable, must be allowed to make decisions for themselves to take risks even if 'sensible experts' might disagree.

Care as a career

Good staff are the critical success factor for care providers. There are immense difficulties in obtaining staff of the required quality because of the high cost, particularly, of housing, especially in the south-east of England. Providers should work together through organisations such as local care associations and Skills for Care to develop social care as an attractive career.

Mental health

Many mental health conditions, not just dementia, are major problems for older people. People with dementia are often depressed (not just unhappy because of their circumstances e.g. loss of health) and providers must train staff to be aware of these separate but interlinked issues.

Competition and co-operation

Providers are often the most passionate advocates for their clients (and are not as often portrayed, money-grabbing entrepreneurs only out to make money for themselves). In these challenging times, although they are essentially competitors, providers can and should co-operate where mutual benefit can be identified – support your local care association.

"Residential care is important and in the best interests of many individuals ... when their needs become too great or when they want it (for company, for example)."

The importance of community

Loneliness is literally a killer. Older people waste away for want of friendship and human contact. While, in an ideal world, extended families would provide that support, I don't think that the UK will go as far as China and pass a law requiring families to visit elderly relatives. So, for many older people care, in communal settings is (part of?) the answer.

Promotion of all-round wellbeing

A good retirement setting, like Whiteley Village, addresses the physical, social and emotional (or spiritual) wellbeing of its residents. Meaningful activity is a critical component but not just what the provider thinks would be fun (or easy to organise!). When they can, activities should be run by clients for clients, supported by staff or volunteers.

Keep the generations mixed

While many older people like the company of other (as they see it) like-minded people there is the danger of creating a 'grey ghetto' so every effort must be made to keep care settings engaged with the local community and to keep all the generations mixing. (See "When Teenage Meets Old Age" http://www.youtube.com/watch?v=Zkwfb1RcNYs)

Ten lessons learnt by a regulatory lawyer

PETER GROSE

is head of healthcare, Lester Aldridge LLP Solicitors. Peter acts as a specialist lawyer for a number of national and regional care providers and also for the national care associations, the NCA and RNHA.

I have been a lawyer acting for care providers, large and small, for nearly 25 years. I have dealt with situations ranging from safeguarding investigations right through to regulators making emergency applications before a magistrate seeking to immediately cancel a provider's registration. There are a number of themes throughout those 25 years which I would like to share:

Good managers must be treasured!

Most problems occur in homes without a registered manager. Often providers do not realise how good a manager is until he or she has left. Standards drop without consistent management and having a number of interim managers, none of whom makes it through to registration.

Even good managers need mentoring and supervision

Do not think that a manager can run a home in isolation. A registered provider needs to have regular contact throughout the week so that there can be dialogue on issues which might turn into regulatory problems, such as staff recruitment, training and essential repairs to the home.

Inspections are a snapshot in time

You may have an excellent CQC report but this might date from a time when you had a longstanding manager who has since left. Alternatively, the inspection could have been cursory and covered only a few of the Essential Standards of Quality and Safety. Do not rest on your laurels! Consider having a trial inspection of regulatory standards by an experienced independent consultancy.

Pre-admission assessments

Do not skimp on your pre-admission assessments. Resist the temptation to admit a resident who is beyond the capacity of your staff's existing skillset, even if you have a number of empty beds. Serious regulatory problems could result.

Recording and record keeping

If something goes wrong, commissioners, safeguarding authorities and CQC will judge you on how accurately you have recorded the chain of events leading up to an incident, whether it be a resident falling out of bed or the wrong drug being administered. Make sure your staff, whether permanent or agency, fully understand the importance of recording fully, carefully and accurately. Shortage of time is no excuse.

Staff training – especially safeguarding

Leading on from the last point, your staff (and by extension your residents) deserve the best possible training. Ensure that all staff are fully trained and have updates on their training. This includes knowing when to invoke safeguarding procedures and recording and reporting safeguarding incidents appropriately.

Safeguarding meetings – always take notes!

Safeguarding investigations are getting increasingly common. If you are invited to a safeguarding meeting, either as a provider or manager, be sure to take very careful notes of what is discussed because the local authorities take weeks to issue the minutes. Good notes protect your position.

Inspectors are seldom completely wrong

While inspectors sometimes misjudge issues, the vast majority highlight issues which are of genuine concern. It is usually counterproductive to blame an adverse inspection entirely on the inspector.

Case History

A care provider consulted me after a poor CQC inspection report, which triggered a safeguarding investigation. The provider had previously received excellent reports but a longstanding manager had retired and there had been difficulties in recruiting a suitable new manager. After advice, the provider put an action plan in place, a new manager was registered and the embargo on referrals soon lifted.

Talk with fellow providers and keep your knowledge base up

A problem shared is a problem halved. Join a national or local care association and share common issues. Most associations also provide a forum for training.

Seek legal advice sooner rather than later

As lawyers, we are often unable to take as effective action as we would wish because the provider has come to us too late. Contact an experienced care regulatory lawyer as soon as you have a suspicion of a problem.

What working with people living with dementia has taught me

Prof. Graham Stokes

is director of dementia care at Bupa Care Services and honorary visiting professor of person-centred dementia care, University of Bradford.

The question 'What has working with people living with dementia taught me?' is a question of our times, for not that long ago such a question would rarely ,if ever, have been contemplated. It would not have crossed people's minds because the prevailing opinion was that such enquiry was an irrelevance: was it not the case that a person with dementia was first buried under layers of intellectual devastation, and then later destined to one day disappear? Alzheimer's Disease was a terrible condition, it destroyed the person but forgot to take the body away – a body that thereafter solely played host to signs and symptoms of disease. How wrong we were:

A person nevertheless

We work with people whose intellectual powers are failing yet, as time passes and their dementia becomes severe, remain like you and I – people who are made up of a rich tapestry of needs, wants and emotions.

Complex, as we all are

We are all complicated. Our partners, family and friends may at times be mystified by our conduct. We at times may surprise ourselves, asking 'why did I do that?', and are sometimes mystified by the answer. So why should a person with dementia be anything other than similarly complicated in what they say and do?

All are resourced differently

Just as each person embarks on their own journey into dementia and each is resourced differently, so some will cope less well than others. Consequently, on occasions we are given the opportunity to wonder at the extraordinary fortitude of the human spirit.

We share so much in common

We work with people who are unique but with whom we share more in common – fundamental human needs and emotions, some innate, others the product of early learning – than that which separates us.

A psychology shared by all

What all people share embraces a need to feel safe, to have a sense of belonging, to be in receipt of tenderness and affection, to be occupied, to have meaningful not cursory human contact, to experience self-respect and tragically, given the nature of dementia, a need to know all is well, akin to peace of mind.

The guiding principle

The person living with dementia cannot be ignored but instead, in all instances and at all times, knowing who they are must be the guiding principle that governs whatever we do to help them negotiate what can be a harrowing journey into and through a world of not knowing.

Not all what it seems

The person may often appear different, but it is misguided to take this as evidence that the person has disappeared, leaving behind nothing more than a shell or shadow of little consequence. While appearances may support such an assertion, my experience is that appearances can be deceptive!

Our purpose: to meet needs

We must endeavour to understand each person with dementia, affirm their value, acknowledge their experience and continually search for ways to meet their needs, even when these are obscure and difficult for them to articulate.

Case History

Grace transcended her dementia with the same spirit she had always displayed. On a journey from certainty to uncertainty, Grace's character was liberated, this time by dementia. Deprived of what we take for granted, Grace again displayed resilience of spirit despite being, or maybe because she was affected by dementia.

Dementia as a disability

No one is all disability, so we must never become preoccupied with a person's dementia to the exclusion of all else. If we do, all we see is difference, and if all we see is difference then we think we share nothing in common. The danger then is that we start to play their life by a set of rules we would not wish to have applied to our own.

A final thought

Our reappraisal of dementia was not the consequence of an elegant scientific break-through. It came about through appreciating the experiences of people attempting to live their lives in the face of awful debilitating brain disease, people who only years previously were living lives indistinguishable from our own, blissfully ignorant of the fact that before too long they were to face a life affected by dementia. I wonder how many people reading these words will end their lives similarly.

How I learned to be myself at work and what it taught me

CHRIS MANTHORP

was a psychiatric nurse, became a residential care manager and moved rapidly to senior management. He is now a consultant and writer.

My first management role was running a home for people living with dementia and behavioural problems. It was a terrific home but I wasn't enjoying my role. I put a distance between myself and my work, acting out my stereotypical image of a manager. I suddenly realised that not being myself at work impacted on care and its delivery. It was a burden. It diverted energy. I would fight better battles for the libertarian approach to care I believe in if I was upfront and personal. I had to be more myself if I was going to get things changed.

Insist on freedom

If you bring with you what you really are to work you will be more comfortable and more productive. Something as trivial as wearing clothes I wanted to wear - earring, baggy trousers and kaleidoscopic ties in those days, I regret to say – rather than what was expected meant that I relaxed and brought more passion to the role. I was a better carer and manager. More importantly, I started insisting on the greatest possible freedom for the people we were supporting, which really improved their quality of life.

Building a fraternity

You will grow faster as a manager and a person, meeting people who are interested in your views and who have interesting views themselves. There's a fraternity between people putting their lives into their work.

Stick to your guns

It isn't easy. I found I alarmed some of my staff and annoyed some of my managers, who expected conformism and risk avoidance. The home could get a little wild, too. I stuck to my guns, however.

Be sincere

Your sincerity will convince others: it's much easier to argue for and achieve things you really believe in. Even when you fail you'll know you were right to try.

Work/life balance

Passion has a down side you have to be prepared for: the boundary between your private life and your work blurs, which can be hard on family. It's worth struggling to find new ways of balancing life and work if you care about what you do.

Relationships require balance

Being open isn't the same as relentless honesty or bleeding all over your workmates. It's about putting your beliefs into your workplace and how you conduct your relationships.

Explore the limits

It's sensible to draw boundaries – few people long to know the intimate details of your life - but it's sensible to explore towards them, too. Relationships based on honesty at work get things done, and give people a much stronger sense that what they're doing is worthwhile. If you overstep the mark you can always put it right – people are generally pretty tolerant.

"We are our choices."

– Jean-Paul Sartre

Treat people as people

The biggest impact being more myself at work had was on my relationship with residents. I got closer to them. In my previous role as a psychiatric nurse manager, I noticed the two most effective ward staff were unqualified nursing assistants. What they had to offer patients was what they were as people and their generosity of spirit. It's much easier to treat people as people – the core of good care – if you ignore the patient/nurse, well/ill roles as much as you can. Most of the time concepts like that get in the way of relationships based on personhood and shared humanity.

Make an impact

I owe my subsequent career to that moment of decision. I'm a writer these days. I know many people that I couldn't have conceived of knowing at that time. I have a (possibly deluded) sense that I contribute to the way the sector thinks about itself. Making that original decision allowed me to become more serious about my work and to make an impact.

2

What's it like being...

What it's like being a care home manager

JACQUELINE JEYNES qualified as a nurse from Northampton General Hospital in 1981, continuing her nursing career to date in various posts within the healthcare profession, most recently as group operations support manager with Avery Healthcare.

Under the umbrella of being a 'care home manager' is a multi-faceted role which draws on academic, professional and lifelong learning and experience. The ability to metamorphose without warning from one role to another, rather like the proverbial caterpillar to butterfly, in the blink of an eye and to engage effectively is paramount, as life in a care home is far from predictable.

Diversity and challenge

While being a care home manager is most rewarding it is as equally perplexing, through the diversity of the challenges that it brings.

Nurturing staff

The biggest challenge is making sure that the team of staff through which you work are diligent, observant, caring, supportive, skilled, passionate in all that their position entails and are compliant in their duties. After all, carers aren't born to the job – they are individuals from society's diverse social spectrum who need to be recruited and trained.

Compliance

There are so many other challenges that a care home manager faces, namely the compliance of the care home to the requirements of those who regulate the service, its stakeholders, the residents and relatives, the staff group and your responsibility to your employer in ensuring that the home is both compliant and financially viable, but to name a few! Life can be pressured...

Priorities and balance

The ability to be able to safely prioritise the workload and find solutions to potential problems in the future is key. This ability is vital not only to the overall success of the care home but is also important to the manager's working life and personal life which must be in balance. The role is totally encompassing, both in time and energy and it is easy to throw yourself so wholeheartedly into the role that you quickly find yourself far out along the line to being 'burnt out'. So moderation and proportion have to be applied.

Frustrations

There can also be frustrations resulting from internal politics and the inevitable differences and discrepancies which happen when people work together.

Rewards

While the role can be challenging and even occasionally frustrating, there is also great pride to be taken, and the satisfaction of a job well done when you receive words of gratitude from those that are in your care, their relatives, or from those that are in your employ to whom you have given opportunities of learning and/or promotion.

Decision-making

Being a care home manager is a huge position of trust and, like all positions of responsibility, there is the potential for legal and professional problems. These could be onerous and are never far from one's mind in any decision-making process. The ability, therefore, to network within supportive and appropriate communities and to learn from the experiences and skills of others is fundamental, not only to your own wellbeing and success, but to those who to whom you have a duty of care and responsibility.

"Teamwork is the framework to success."

– ANON.

Pride in positive outcomes

As a care home manager you have the opportunity to dispel the myths and suspicion that frequently cloud the care home sector by the negative publicity aroused by the media. There is the opportunity to demonstrate through the good practices of your own care home and staff that those who live in care homes *do* experience positive outcomes and lead fulfilled and enriched lives. For many individuals it is often the case that this hasn't been their norm for a number of years; having to struggle to cope with the pressure of daily living activities in their own homes on their own.

Embracing change

Being a care home manager is also a position which gives you the autonomy to evoke and embrace change, to realise your vision of all that you would wish for as an older person yourself. It is an opportunity to impart your knowledge and skills to others, it is a position of creativity in which the older person is ultimately the beneficiary.

A position of influence

The ambience of a care home comes from within and from those who work and live there, and it is fantastic to be in a position to influence this.

What it's like being a chef

SAMANTHA WHYTE

is head chef at Hunters Care Centre, Cirencester. She progressed from trainee to head chef after completing her training with the Barchester chef academy.

Being a chef in a care home is extremely rewarding, catering for all types of diets, likes and dislikes, allergies and intolerances. You see the enjoyment of our residents when you cook them their favourite food. We love spending time with residents, finding out what lovely homemade dishes they want. No two days are ever the same as there is always something happening; from someone's birthday to a visit from a special friend and we love to cater for them all. Food is so important and we aim to make every mealtime a social and enjoyable occasion.

Modified diets

Chefs in care homes need to have a passion to serve food that they will be proud of and this includes modified meals such as thick puree and fork mashable meals. These must be as appetising as the original meal. Colour, contrast and texture are so important for everyone.

Freshly prepared foods

Fresh, seasonal foods should be of the highest quality. Start with great produce to make mouth-watering, tasty and nutritious meals. Lovely home cooked food stimulates the appetite so the residents are ready to enjoy their meal. You can even involve residents in cooking; whether chopping carrots or kneading bread.

Having fun

It's great fun cooking the foods that our residents want to eat; foods they like and that remind them of their younger days. Asking residents what they enjoyed at school, what their mums cooked for them and family favourites; and producing those dishes is such fun.

Being charitable

Being a chef might be hard work but we always find time to bake cakes for fetes, supporting the community for coffee mornings, or making jams and chutneys for the local W.I. The care home is integral to the community.

Supporting others

In any team there is a mix of skills; each person should be encouraged to develop their skills and show off what they are learning. It's great to see young trainee chefs practising their skills by cooking what they are learning for the residents; the residents reap the benefits!

My collection of shoes

Chefs have a life too and our residents want to hear about that life; they want to see funky shoes, or pink hair, they love to see and hear about the latest fashion. Don't exclude them when you are going on a special date and trying to decide what to wear. Remember they have a life-time of experience; you might just spark a special memory.

How do you like your eggs in the morning?

Every new resident must be visited by the chef on arrival to find out what they like to eat and what they don't like. The smallest things can make the biggest difference whether it is browned toast or a runny egg, pasta or potatoes, Brussels sprouts or broccoli; it's so important to get it just right.

Mavis's lemon drizzle cake

There will always be one resident who will have a better recipe than you; their years of experience will result in that perfect lemon drizzle cake or shortbread. Let them cook it; or alternatively cook it for them using their own recipe.

"One cannot think well, love well, sleep well, if one has not dined well."

– VIRGINIA WOOLF

High days and holidays

You can always find time to cook for that special event; a picnic, a saint's day, a birthday, a themed event; the residents should always have a party to look forward to, with a different theme to make it a memorable experience. Chefs love cooking something different, from spinning pizzas to flambéing crepes.

Hydrate

Remember hydration is an essential part of nutrition. You can make nutritious fortified drinks, or cooling refreshing fresh juices. You can whip up delicious smoothies, delectable ice creams or delightful sorbets. Don't forget they might love their gin and tonic too.

What it's like being a finance director

NEIL TAYLOR

is finance and development director for international development markets at Bupa. His previous role was finance and development director for Bupa Care Services.

The operational and commercial success of a care home depends on the skills and ability of home managers and senior staff who necessarily must have a good grasp of the financial aspects of running a business effectively. Excellent customer care and a positive, enjoyable working environment cannot be separated from good financial management in successful businesses. The finance director is responsible for ensuring that the financial affairs of the organisation meet legal and regulatory requirements, as well as expertly advising the board and/or owners about business performance and key issues. In the care services world, the finance director depends on managers to keep good, accurate financial records and information. Creating the operating framework to enable this to happen relies upon clear policies and procedures but, most of all, upon excellent clear communication between care managers and finance directors to ensure they obtain appropriate support and guidance.

Keep it simple

Smart systems, uncomplicated processes and easy-to-understand policies and procedures make it simpler for all staff to effectively carry out their business and ensure financial records are accurate. Without these, the financial controls and management information required to effectively manage an organisation's finances are jeopardised and the finance director cannot effectively do his job.

The customer is king

Understanding and meeting, or exceeding, customers' needs is paramount. High quality care and associated support to relatives and funders is critical in establishing favourable relationships and reputations. Ensuring that there is a clear understanding of the financial terms of service provision contracts reduces the likelihood of possible disputes which can be stressful and damaging for all, and the finance director is ultimately the key person responsible for this.

Cash is queen

Without cash, businesses fail, and understanding where and when cash comes from, and where it goes to, is critical in understanding the fundamentals of a commercial operation. Managers understanding the value of cash along with accurate records of all financial transactions will ensure that the operation maintains a positive cash flow.

Sources of income

The complexity of care funding means that understanding whether it is the local authority, NHS, individuals, pensions, insurance, or family members (or in some cases all of these) who are paying for services is essential in enabling good relationships and effective billing. An incorrect or late bill can adversely affect relationships and potentially lead to legal disputes that can damage reputations and embroil both finance directors and managers unnecessarily.

Payments

In care management, staff costs are often the main cost followed by third party suppliers. Managers correctly certifying staff's working hours and pay enhancements along with the accurate authorisation of goods and services supplied, will ensure payments are accurate and staff and suppliers are satisfied.

Asset management

Investing in staff training, career development and wellbeing is as essential as investing in maintaining and enhancing the physical aspects of a care home. Managers able to ensure that investment is sufficient to maintain these assets to the desired standards mitigates against the need for the finance director to look at expensive replacements or re-provision.

Regulatory and legal compliance

Complying with laws and regulatory needs is mandatory to ensure finance directors and managers are not held to account in court, and remain out of jail. Ensuring paper accounts are kept, tax records are maintained, financial controls are effective, laws are not broken, and regulations are met will all help to create an effective operation and a positive reputation.

"We are what we repeatedly do. Excellence, therefore, is not an act, but a habit."

– ARISTOTLE

Management information

From care plans to personnel records, staff rostering to food stocks, or unpaid invoices to wage costs, good quality relevant information helps the correct decisions to be made. This enables both care managers and finance directors to focus on the key areas of customer service delivery and future opportunities.

Painless refinancing

The value of a care business is typically linked to its financial performance and the quality of the environment. Ensuring that both are healthy enables financial obligations to be minimised and refinancing requirements, normally led by the finance director, to be painless.

Opportunity costs

Care management, like life, involves choosing between alternatives since resources are ultimately limited. Assessing correctly whether to serve customer A or B, appoint Mandy or Jacqui, invest in staff or equipment, choose bacon or egg will help navigate a business to success. This ability has never been more relevant than in today's challenging world.

What it's like being a healthcare assistant

ANNE SMITH

has worked in the care profession for more 30 years. She is currently a senior health care assistant at Richmond Village, Northampton.

Fulfilling, demanding, stressful at times – that's how I would describe what being a senior health care assistant is like. Why do I do this job? – I get great pleasure and satisfaction when I see a client's face light up or a client's relative looking satisfied with the standard of care I have provided and knowing that however small it may be, I have played my part in ensuring the care clients receive is of the highest standard and they obtain the level of care that you or I would expect for ourselves or a loved one.

Supervision of staff

Staff need to be set structured standard tasks. Each shift I myself am hands-on and work on the floor with staff to ensure high standards of care are always given. If any issues or concerns arise the staff will inform me immediately and I can deal with the problem.

Training courses for staff

I hold training courses for staff members, which I feel very passionate about. The courses are informative and relaxed. The feedback from team members is always positive and interaction between the team is excellent. Knowledge from courses is put to good use.

Attending external courses

I enjoy attending training courses to obtain further knowledge which I pass on to my team to enable us to give our clients the highest standard of care at all times. Training courses are important to keep ahead of any changes or legislation that arises from time to time.

Talking to management

I feel communication is vital for staff and management to ensure that the running of the care home is of a high standard and accidents and or incidents are minimised.

Management support

As a staff member I feel and know we do have management's support if needed. You are never greeted by, "what can I do for you again?" – you are listened to and full support is given. We all work for the same company and if you have a happy crew, staff will give a good performance. Our management are not hidden behind closed doors in their air conditioned offices – their doors are always open.

Out and about

When escorting clients to appointments e.g. hospital, clinics and dental appointments, I believe their well-being is paramount so I always ensure safe transport and that all their needs are taken care of, again ensuring the utmost level of care, while always remembering you are representing the company.

Handovers to staff

As a senior health care assistant it is imperative at each shift change I pass on any information I feel will assist the staff members in the efficient running of the home and personal care of the clients.

Daily routines

The senior care assistant's role changes from day-to-day depending on what is happening on the unit – these include the allocation of staff duties to ensure clients' personal needs are tended to and with many years' experience I try to pass on my knowledge.

Case History

Client Mr X enjoys a glass or two (or three!) of wine and to encourage him to drink more fluids in the day I found that serving fruit juice in a wine glass helped! This helped to increase his fluid intake and improved his hydration levels.

First days in the job

I have found it beneficial to familiarise myself with the medical information and the life case history of all the clients in my care and to learn their likes and dislikes and to interact and gain their trust so a rapport can be built up quickly.

Challenges

The greatest challenge I come across in my job is to keep my colleagues motivated and active during a long shift. I try to lead by example and keep the team's spirits up and portray a positive image at all times.

What it's like being an inspector

At a reception at the Houses of Parliament, the CQC Service User Reference Panel (SURP) member put it best: *'Don't buy into the industry of demonstrating compliance. The inspector who turns up at your door is interested in the same thing you are. Is the care good?'* Don't throw out your evidence files, but think about what is important. It's not paperwork. Methods of regulation can come and go. The advice below is not designed to be a definitive guide or to enable you to try and second guess your inspector. It is a set of principles from personal experience which I hope will help you.

PHILIP KING

is a nurse and barrister with 27 years experience of working in health and social care. He has advised the Law Society on law reform and policy in mental health and disability and has been a director of nursing. Until recently he was director of regulatory development at the Care Quality Commission.

The first 15 steps –

Just stop for a moment. Go outside of your care home. Close your eyes. Try and imagine that you have never been inside before. Now walk in, keeping your eyes, ears, brain, and yes, your nose engaged. What are your impressions? Remember we can all get used to the unacceptable.

Be your own inspector

Let's extend this first principle. If possible try and conduct your own inspection as though you were a new inspector. Better still get your staff to do this with you. Ask a colleague from another care home to help and offer to return the favour.

What to look for

Inspectors will first of all want to talk to residents, relatives, visitors and staff. They will want to hear their honest views and reflections. Only then will they cross-check policies, care plans and so on. This doesn't mean drilling your staff. It means thinking about an honest and open culture.

The five questions

The inspector will be guided by five essential questions. Keep these in mind in all that you and your staff do when you go about your daily work. Are services:
Safe?
Effective?
Caring?
Responsive?
Well-led?

So what . . .

OK, so its back to the paperwork. Yes you still need some of it. Ask yourself "so what... does this demonstrate?.... so what... is its purpose?... so what does this tell me?" It's best to rely on good patient/resident specific documents like care plans, medicines records, patient/residents records and other important records like staff rotas.

Decisions, decisions!

One of the biggest areas of concern relates to the capacity of residents to make their own decisions, and how you deal with situations where the person can't make their own decisions. Make sure you and your staff understand the principles of consent and mental capacity.

What do they know?

Inspectors, before they come to you, will have looked at what intelligence they have. Without wishing to be 'cosy' there will be opportunities to talk through what intelligence they have about your care home.

"The problem is that services need to stop trying to look *good and concentrate on* being *good."*

MEMBER OF *CQC's* SERVICE USER REFERENCE PANEL (SURP)

Risk, what risk?

Demonstrate that you have systems that work in spotting risk in order to take action. Common areas of concern are: staffing and having the right staff who are appropriately trained and up-to-date; medicines management, and lack of meaningful activity and engagement for residents.

Engage

Every inspector's worst case scenario is a disastrous failure in care or a terrible example of abuse. What we know about these cases is that one common factor is a lack of transparency and a culture of isolation. To combat these challenges engage your local community, foster links with schools and community groups.

Beware of experts

Don't get caught up with so-called experts selling you a system that will take care of all your compliance and inspection worries. Such systems don't exist – this approach is outmoded and it is not what inspectors will look for. Take heed of my SURP colleague.

What it's like being a line manager

DAWN HAMILTON

works as a quality assurance manager with HC-One.

She strongly believes that one person can make a difference.

When people ask "what is it you do exactly?" I sometimes struggle to describe the diversity and huge scope of my role. During my nurse training I was once described as being as versatile as an egg and this, along with stamina, resilience and empathy are some of the skills needed to be a good line manager. You need to have the ability to change your management style to suit the situation. Through the following key points I have captured what I feel are the challenges facing my managers and me, along with the pressures and demands of their role.

I wish you didn't work so hard

Care home managers are not 9-5 people; they work really hard to ensure residents have a good quality of life. But this often means they don't get a good balance between work and life. Spending more time at work isn't the answer; being more efficient and working smarter is.

I wish you had the confidence to believe in yourself

Managers in general are humble and don't always have the confidence to tell people what a good job they do. I want my managers to be proud of their achievements and their homes and actively promote this.

I wish you had told me how you were feeling

Often managers feel they are the only ones struggling and that their peers are doing a better job than them. My job is to gain their trust and help them to be open about how they feel. Talking about the pressures and challenges can make it easier to cope when things are not going well.

Why didn't you ask for help?

Asking for help shouldn't be seen as a failure in your abilities, no-one will think any less of you. Let me help: that's what I'm there for and we can make a difference together.

Why do you always see your cup as half empty?

A pessimistic attitude and dwelling on problems can affect your ability to move forward positively and efficiently. Your attitude affects your team. Focus on your learning and your achievements; you will be surprised how powerful this can be.

Why won't they listen to me?

Struggling to communicate exactly what it is you want from staff can be a challenge. What you perceive you have told them can be entirely different to what they have heard. Make sure you devote time to help your team know what's expected of them.

I wish I had dealt with that at the time

Dealing with people issues at the time makes it easier to do your job well. Don't put off situations which may be unpleasant. Take control and be assertive.

Why do you find it so hard to delegate?

Many managers feel the need to do everything themselves! Time spent coaching others will lead to a lighter workload for you and a trained, motivated team.

Why don't you answer my emails?

Poor time management, missing deadlines and giving evasive answers are all signs of bad management. Don't become the manager who always needs to be chased!

Why didn't you tell me?

Be open and transparent; keeping people informed will lead to less complaints. Good communication will ensure you receive the advice and support to enable you to handle difficult situations.

""I am a woman who is suddenly aware that I can control my destiny by creating that I most wish to have"

– MOLINARY, 2012

(AS LINE MANAGERS WE HAVE THE ABILITY TO CREATE THIS FOR OUR RESIDENTS.)

The role of a managing director

Julien Payne

is owner and managing director of Titleworth Healthcare Ltd.

I have ultimate responsibility – not only for the wellbeing of my staff and the company's commercial viability, but for the protection and welfare of our highly vulnerable and totally dependent residents. This creates a dramatically different dimension. Additionally, the fundamental commercial and regulatory principles and constraints are unfamiliar concepts to staff involved in a care environment – their priority, as it should be, is the wellbeing of their residents. My particular challenge is to balance their essential caring approach with the necessary commercial demands to ensure they understand the influence this may have on decisions.

There's no such thing as 'off duty'

I was brought up in a family devoted to care, my parents created the Titleworth company based around a single care home – my grandmother's house. From the age of eight I did every job, helped with every resident. Now I have two young sons of my own and want to spend quality time with them. But how can I put aside the ultimate responsibility for nearly 300 dependent residents and the dedicated teams that look after them? This is no ordinary management role, it's certainly not one for the faint-hearted but it has so many magical moments.

Happy staff means happy residents

My staff have an inner force that gets them through every day, no matter what they have to face. My challenge is not to de-motivate them or dampen their enthusiasm by burdening them with the issues and constraints involved in keeping the company profitable – it is to keep their concentration on doing what they do so well, which is caring for our residents. They are the heart of the business after all, so I need to manage the commercial side in such a way as to let them do their jobs to the best of their ability.

The best feeling – magic moments with residents and relatives

When I see our residents looking content and happy, or when I get a heartfelt word of thanks from a relative or a cheeky smile from a resident, I know we are getting it right. It's moments like these that make it all worthwhile.

Being patient when everything takes longer than I would like it to

There are so many things I want to improve but I know change can't happen overnight. To make effective changes, I need to get everyone involved, but the demands of caring for frail, elderly and disorientated residents, mean that implementing change takes time, patience and careful planning.

Government decisions have a profound impact on how care can be provided

Government just doesn't understand the effects its pronouncements have on our operations, nor realise the damage their decisions inflict on the care sector and ultimately the residents. We will not compromise the level of care we provide, but I am constantly compelled to make tough decisions.

Negative publicity 'tars all care homes with the same brush'

My homes really are different – they are true 'homes from home', but I find it hard to take when we are all judged the same by the media. Our hard-earned reputation can be so easily damaged when standards elsewhere are found to be unacceptable.

Keeping up with the ever-changing needs in the care sector – ordeal or opportunity?

It's a constant challenge keeping up with the trends – but being 'ahead of the game' and able to anticipate requirements is essential to provide the range of services that funders are looking for.

"A leader is best when people barely know he exists, when his work is done, his aim fulfilled, they will say: we did it ourselves."

– Lao Tzu

Think and act positive

My staff carry out their duties efficiently and with a cheerfulness I know they can't always feel because their residents come first – so knowing that attitudes affect everyone, how can I allow myself the luxury of 'a bad day'?

Bankers don't view success in the same way as carers

If you're not immersed in the care world, it's hard to understand what keeps us going. Daily routines are tough, often harrowing, with death a constant reality. That means 'success' to us is often very different to the criteria bankers use.

Sharing the passion

If I didn't have a genuine passion for this business, I couldn't carry on. The best reward is when I see my managers feeling that same passion and transferring it to their staff, which in turn puts a smile on the face of every resident!

What it's like being a registered nurse

PHIL BENSON

is a registered nurse and deputy manager of EachStep Blackley, a specialist integrated dementia care service in Manchester, operated by Community Integrated Care.

Working in nursing is a privileged position. To me, there is no greater satisfaction than being able to help someone when they are at their most vulnerable, or to assist someone to fulfil their greatest potential. I believe that the foundation of exceptional nursing care begins with a deep appreciation and understanding of the people you support. By getting to know them as individuals, recognising their personal identity and values, nurses can deliver true person-centred care and achieve the best outcomes possible. I have tried here to capture some of the important principles of life-enhancing, relationship-focused nursing care.

Reflect on decisions

Working on the frontline of a dementia service is extremely fast paced. People's needs can change rapidly and decisions have to be made quickly. I continually have to ask myself: "Would this person make this decision, if they were able to?"

Not just a workplace

To me, the service I work in is far more than 'just the place that I go to do my job'. It is a person's home; I'm there to get to know the people who live in it and to help them achieve the highest quality of life possible.

Value life legacies

If you know the person you support and their life history, you can develop a great connection and deliver true person-centred care. Don't just learn the basic facts of their life, uncover who they really are and the important relationships that they value. Strive to apply this knowledge creatively to the care that you deliver.

Be open to opportunities

Being part of a forward-thinking organisation allows me to seize opportunities to improve outcomes. To deliver great care, you need to be creative, open to new experiences and totally focused on the person you are supporting as an individual.

Attentiveness counts

Care homes can be isolated from rapid access to primary or secondary care. Nurses need to be attentive to identify heath concerns at their earliest stage and decisive in making the call for additional support.

Lead by example

Nursing teaches you a lot about leadership. Being a good leader can make the difference between achieving a really great outcome or not. I have found that leading by example is essential – if I go the extra mile for the people we support, then so will my team.

Collaborate with others

It's important to have links with your entire local health and social care community – whether that is local mental health teams, Clinical Commissioning Groups or partnership groups, such as community forums or action alliances. Being part of a wider network has allowed me to learn from, and be inspired by, other passionate people.

Strive to better yourself

Nurses should never stop learning. We should always endeavour to take the next step, learn the next skill, and fulfil the next challenge. Always asking myself "Is this the best way?" has helped me to develop new skills and enhance my knowledge.

"Logic will get you from A to B. Imagination will take you everywhere."

– Albert Einstein

A personal ambition

My career goal is simply to make a difference in people's lives – in any given day this could be making someone smile, helping them to eat a meal, or it could be saving a life.

Care about caring

Every day when I come into work, I try to give it my all, taking my time to provide care to people in a way that they would choose. By putting the people that we support first and being aspirational, nurses can support people to achieve amazing things.

What it's like being a relative

DENNIS FULLER

is a retired army brigadier.

In 1956 I met a lovely, charming, tall girl called Monica. She had just returned from four years in New Zealand. I was a young captain serving in the army with her brother. Monica and I were married in 1957 – both aged 27. I retired in 1984 as a brigadier. While in the army Monica was a dedicated, loyal, wonderful wife and supported me on postings to England, Wales, Scotland and seven foreign countries. We had 22 army homes and were blessed with two lovely children, Mark and Kim and now have five grandchildren. We moved to Hereford in 1987 and ten years later Monica began to show signs of dementia.

Dementia awareness

In 2001 Monica began to show signs of memory loss and had several painful falls. My first aim was to get her to see an excellent GP. He immediately referred her to a memory clinic which made an assessment that Monica had dementia. A hospital scan confirmed Alzheimer's.

Understanding Alzheimer's

What is that? How does it progress? Absolutely shattered I joined the Alzheimer's Society. A dedicated psychiatric nurse gave sound advice and made arrangements for respite care. This was a life saver. We joined the monthly Alzheimer's Companionship Club. It was a great comfort and I still have friends who are members.

Acceptance

We both agreed to be open and not ashamed to announce Monica had Alzheimer's. Our friends were understanding and supportive. Monica continued her volunteer work at the hospice charity shop. She had volunteered for 12 years. This allowed me to spend a morning playing golf!

Lifestyle

We continued our weekly church attendance, supermarket shop, daily walks, lunches out and quiet evenings at home. We enjoyed visits from our family. A useful ploy when meeting strangers was to wear an Alzheimer's wrist band and unobtrusively point to it as a sign of Monica's condition.

Sole carer

Retired and fit I was Monica's sole carer for six years, I had to learn unfamiliar skills – cooking, laundry, incontinence care, bathing and dressing Monica. She was prescribed Remenol and loaned aids to help her with eating and getting out of the bath.

Behavioural change

Inevitably Monica's health deteriorated. She had more falls, developed challenging behavior, asked continually for her mother and in respite care was leader of the 'escape committee'! A week before our 50th Anniversary Party she had a severe urinary infection, collapsed and had to be hospitalised.

Nursing care

After a week in hospital she was transferred to Ross Community Hospital and while there we were interviewed by matron and the physiotherapist from Hampton Grange nursing home and offered a place. To confine my darling wife to a home was the hardest decision I had to make.

Daily routine

Monica is now bed-bound and welcomes me with her eyes. I visit daily, give her a blessing and then cranberry juice, manuka honey, liquidised lunch, a bifidus actiregularis yoghurt and dessert. It is a labour of love supported by family, friends and a wonderful nursing care team.

"Never give in."

– General Sir Henry Lawrence , who was Governor of Punjab when he founded his school in 1847.

Care home

Our care home is welcoming, comfortable, well-run and situated overlooking the River Wye. The staff are cheerful, friendly and caring. Monica has a single room, a good personal care plan, daily food and liquid intake charts. The home has an excellent ongoing training scheme and appetising menus. Monica is comfortable and content.

Care and facilities

The home offers a wide range of facilities – TV, hairdressing, chiropody and physiotherapy to name a few. Each weekday has a planned activity. I am pleased to support the themed parties and to be accepted as a member of their team. I donated an Alzheimer's library to the home. I'm a very fortunate relative and am deeply grateful to have found Hampton Grange!

What it's like being a resident

Dr Ann Johnson MBE

is a trained nurse and was a nurse tutor/lecturer in nursing for many years. She speaks throughout the country about living with Alzheimer's disease.

I was diagnosed with Alzheimer's Disease when I was 52. After living with my mother she was unable to care for me so we both decided I should move to a care home. Recognise that I am in your care and am totally dependent on you. Listen to my innermost thoughts – you will see them as you get to know me. Ensure there is someone I can 'open my heart to' and discuss personal things with. I will love you and give you my respect and gratitude. Show me you love and care for me and that you are with me.

Know me for who I am

I have a past and a future. Be aware of what my past has involved – parents and who they were. They have made me who I am. My achievements at school, my degrees which I undertook part time while I continued to work.

It is important to know a resident's background

Know I am a trained nurse and was a lecturer in nursing. I had clinical contact with patients in my role. I took early retirement from my job. I enjoyed my career and valued the students who taught me a lot.

Keep up-to-date with dementia training

Know that I have Alzheimer's Disease and how that will affect me now and in the future. Be aware of the care needed and how best that can be given to my satisfaction. Understand my individualities and uniqueness in this.

Understand my condition

Know how my Alzheimer's affects me and the difficulties I have – short term memory, visuospatial difficulties, orientation, word finding. Understand how my frustration arises, how it can be dealt with or prevented.

Support me

Support me through the difficult times by love and support. Show me you love and are with me.

Respect me

Show me dignity and respect for who I am. Understand where my problems might lie and show kindness. Understand my concerns and terrors and that I am terrified of what the future might hold. Respect my religious beliefs and support me in the practice of my faith.

Love and care for me

I go round the country speaking about "living with Alzheimer's". Show an interest and support me in this. Give me confidence and reassurance. Show you love and care for me in all I do. When I can do less, please understand that I need encouragement.

Listen to me

Listen to my innermost thoughts. Understand my innermost feelings which you will be able to do the more you know me. Try to understand my concerns and worries, no matter how strange they may seem to you. Do not take over. Please do not assume anything. Take your cue from me.

Observe me

Ensure I am comfortable in my surroundings. Can I handle things in my room eg taps, toilets, cupboards, fridge. Try and help me to be comfortable and sleep well. Identify when I show signs of illness if I am not able to tell you.

"The three things that keep me going are my friends, my faith and doing my talks. Please understand the sheer terror I live in everyday with my Alzheimer's Disease. So, please love me for who I am. We are ordinary people with a problem. Don't be scared of us."

– Dr Ann Johnson in Sabat S, Johnson A, Swarbrick C and Keady J 2011

Give me practical help

Ensure that I have access to an independent financial advisor all the time I have mental capacity. When this is no longer the case support me when I have enacted my Enduring Power of Attorney. Help me day-to-day with simple things like counting and dealing with money. Make continuous checks on my state of mind. Identify the progression of my Alzheimer's. Be aware of and identify any anxiety in me or inability to deal with life. Be aware of what I need at end of life. Be aware of my prepaid funeral plan. Know my will is kept at my solicitors.

A single care home owner's view

ANNIE SINNOTT MBE

has built her career around caring for people and in 2007 she was awarded an MBE for services to social care.

As a district nurse I met a lot of isolated and lonely older people. This often led to health problems and hospitalisation, and I thought: "There must be a better way than this". I opened The Old Vicarage in 1984 with one resident. After much development we are now a 40-bed home, and have been recognised in many national awards. It pleases me that during my midwifery years I provided good care at the beginning of life, and now I am doing that for people nearing the end of life by creating a secure and homely atmosphere with skilled and dedicated staff.

Legislation

I have always followed legislation. There is a lot more now than there was when I started out, but as a single care home owner I can interpret it to suit my home's environment. We all get frustrated by it, but it is there for a reason.

Communication

I always make sure that all staff really get to know our residents so they never feel isolated. Nothing pleases me more than to see them all sitting together doing a quiz or similar activity. I encourage formal and informal communication – not just verbal, but also visual – so everyone can contribute and nothing gets missed.

Working to budget

I like to do things properly and prove it can be done on a reasonable budget. I see it as a contract between myself and our residents, families, and staff to run a tight ship without stinting on the care and comfort we provide.

Extra touches

As a single care home owner I can do things my way. Little touches in the home make residents happy, like a glass of sherry, traditional china tea sets – and a computer so they can talk to their families on Skype! I always think positively and tell my staff "we can do this", then work out how.

Owner accessibilty

I can do most of the jobs around the home if I have to – it may just take longer! – but I like to be visible so that residents, relatives and staff can approach me about anything which may improve the quality of life. Being independent, we can be flexible in what we provide.

Staff development

I invest a lot in the development of staff members of all ages. Your staff are your shop window and pivotal to providing a good service. Making them feel valued by a simple "Well done", recognising them within the home, or by nominating them for awards has repaid me a thousandfold in the way they carry out their work.

Younger care workers

I enjoy bringing on young people. My two managers came to me as school leavers and have worked hard to get where they are now. They bring fresh ideas and, being local, their commitment provides reassurance to our GPs and to residents and families.

Networking

I find it valuable to network with homes in different locations. Staff also find it helpful. There is always something we can learn from each other.

"My mother has been with you for 12 years, an indication of the care she has received …. As I live so far away it is a wonderful feeling that her health and welfare are more than ably looked after by the whole staff – and they do it with unfailing good humour!"

– CARLIE SOUTHEY DEL FANTE

Engaging with the community

Making links with the community around you helps future residents get to know and trust you and your home. I constantly try to raise the profile of this sector in which there is so much good practice but which rarely receives praise publicly.

Having the right attitude

I always tell staff that their attitude towards their work and those they care for must be positive, interested, and respectful. This means a lot if you are feeling frail and frightened. It makes me really cross if one of our residents is in hospital and on visiting I see a reduced standard of care and staff who are off-hand with them. They deserve better!

3

Key management topics

Leadership is what counts

In the 20th century, the term and idea of 'leadership' became unacceptable and was frequently associated with negative connotations. A more 'sterile', operational and acceptable term 'manager/management' took its place. The two are not the same. Much is written about leadership – its nature, purpose, whether it can be learned or is innate. I won't discuss any of this here. However, I will highlight why in services like social and health care, it is a critical factor standing above all other components that contribute to an excellent service and experience. Leadership is what counts because it defines, nurtures, shapes and sustains a culture that delivers on the promise. This leadership is displayed in every part of the service from catering, housekeeping and property maintenance through to care and administration in the care home itself. Its most fundamental expression is through the care home manager! In larger organisations it is found across all the support functions and line managers.

Dr Chai Patel CBE

is chairman of HC-One, deputy chairman of Care Management Group and previously chief executive of the Priory Group.

Providing the vision

Leadership provides a clear, communicable and accessible vision that everyone wants to make happen. This is not a static vision but one that encompasses and expands. It acts as a guiding light to the ups and downs of daily realities and keeps a focus on the purpose of the endeavour.

Setting the standards

It stands for something in the face of many dilemmas and challenges. It defines what is right and wrong; what is acceptable and unacceptable. It defines the hierarchy of priorities that require courage, integrity and honesty, i.e. in 'person-centric' care, the voice and the choice of the individual defines the priorities, not the efficient operation of the organisation.

Recognition and support

Leadership clearly defines expectations and provides the appropriate resources. It recognises achievements, supports during difficulties but is intolerant of under-performance.

Providing consistency

It builds, nurtures and places demands on all those who are involved in the endeavour to ensure that they are chosen to complement each other. There must be a consistency in beliefs and behaviours of all those who are involved.

Attention to detail

There is a deep attention to detail and a culture of "show me". This attention to detail starts with the leader and pervades the organisation through a sense of pride, not coercion.

Sharing responsibility

The process of delegation (not abdication) creates a shared responsibility. At all times, members of the team ensure that what needs to be done gets done in the right way and at the right time. This creates a 'granular' leadership, i.e. at all levels and all disciplines, people take up the leadership role and ensure the whole team delivers the promised experience.

Finding the right balance

The services of social and health care are defined by the experiences of the recipients and participants (their network of family and friends). Therefore, leadership has to find the right balance between the quality and consistency of the inputs (the processes) as well as the perceived experience and agreed outcomes of the service user and their network.

"Leadership of purpose has the ability to unlock an energy which is differentiated, longer lasting and more generous."
– ANON.

A demanding role

Social and health care is a dynamic, multi-disciplinary service with highly variable needs and requirements to provide a consistently flexible and individual-centric service. It demands strength and energy combined with focus and emotional stability.

Accountability

To ensure transparency, openness and a culture that is accountable and honest requires leadership that demonstrates this at every level. It is quick to acknowledge failure and to learn; and willing to take responsibility and face consequences.

Respect for others

In the end, leadership counts because it creates a culture of purpose, service and promise. It creates a vocation which attracts those people who seek and nurture those values and are intolerant of those who don't. It has at its core, a sense of respect for others and a wish to provide them with the kindest and most professional service.

What the best care homes all have in common

JOHN KENNEDY

graduated from Manchester with a degree in economics. He has since followed a career in social care in both the private and voluntary sectors. As director of care services for the JRF and JRHT he is responsible for a range of services and manages a portfolio of research work on risk and regulation, loneliness, dementia friendly communities and recently investigating 'ipads for care'.

Ever since I worked as a care assistant in the mid-1980s, care homes have been under pressure. The pressure, though, is growing more and more acute as our society ages. Our needs are growing, with more complexity, and our expectations are rising too. It is now time to be really honest with ourselves and recognise that we really need care homes and good ones too! But care homes won't be good by us just telling them or wishing them to be so; kindness and compassion can't just be demanded. Good care homes can only come from a good hegemony based on honesty, shared values and respect. My top ten below is aspirational and reflects not only the attributes of a good care home, one where I would like to 'hear the bell toll', but also the attributes required of the 'society' around it: care homes cannot be 'good' on their own. They cannot be islands.

Values must be held at the top

The culture of the provider organisation is crucial to the ability of the care home to be a good one. The views of the chief executive, expressed privately behind their office door, must reflect the fundamentals of integrity, honesty, mutual respect and humanity in relation to the management of their business. If head office does not reflect these values the care home is fettered from the start.

Qualities of the manager

A confident, empathetic, energetic, capable and kind manager is essential for the good care home. One who leads bravely and understands their own accountability and those of their staff. One who knows when to ask for help and is capable of 'pushing back' when demands become unreasonable. One who is fully supported, practically and emotionally.

Staff must be supported

The staff in the good care home are its heart and model its values. They must be respected, supported, well treated and valued. Their emotional as well as employment needs should be recognised and understood. They *must* be fairly paid, at least the Living Wage!

Clarity of purpose

Good care homes manage risk,regulation and paperwork in an adult way. Crucially they never allow the 'system' and 'bureacracy' to become their main purpose, despite the pressures to do so. Relationships and human beings are their focus.

A community of people

The purpose of the good care home is around the 'people' not the establishment. There is no such thing as a 'good 42-bed care home'. There are however places where 42 individuals live well together, albeit with some ups and downs, and share some communal space, time and company. Food reflects this and is tasty and a pleasure. Good care homes try not to refer to 'the residents' as there is no such homogeneous group.

A home is 'lived in'

The environment in a good care home is clean, tidy and well designed. People live there and it shows, it is obvious that individuals have control over their own space. Any tendency to look and feel like a clinic is resisted.

Engagement

Good care homes are engaged with their community. The local community takes responsibility too and encourages, cherishes and supports. Good care homes are welcoming and are easy and friendly places to visit.

"No man is an Island, entire of itself... because I am involved in mankind... never send to know for whom the bell tolls; It tolls for thee."

– John Donne

Working with the health community

Good care homes have good relationships with the local health community. GPs, district nurses, hospital, consultants. They have respect for each other. They listen to each other, collaborate, understand each others' pressures. All work together to find solutions with the person at the centre.

Working with relatives

Relatives are confident in the values of the good care home. They are able to challenge when needed and to thank. They are able to be relatives. They can let the staff do their job with confidence. They understand that the care home is not a babysitter, and that staff are people too and have their own relationships with the people who live there. Relatives too have an adult relationship with the people of the good care home.

Regulatory support

Commissioners and regulators trust the good care home. They engage in an appreciative way, supporting the care home as a valued part of the 'whole' system. They share their knowledge, experiences and good ideas. They challenge and hold to account but they don't place bureaucratic and ineffectual burdens on them. Especially when things go wrong!

Business can be brutal... never forget this

ALAN FIRTH

has spent virtually his entire career in the care sector. He is executive chairman of Meridian Healthcare, one of the most respected providers of care services to elderly people in the UK.

My mum always said to me "look after the pennies, son, and the pounds will look after themselves". Never before has this saying been more relevant than in the management of a care home. With revenue levels stagnating due to central government austerity measures, it is vital that care home managers control their cost bases in a vice-like grip. Equally, continued investment into both staff and the care home itself are crucial, so it is equally vital that 'value for money' is obtained. I hope my knowledge and experience in these areas upon which I comment will help both the 'old hand' and 'newcomer' to develop and maintain a service, in an asset, which everyone is truly proud of.

Plan

Always have a business plan for your care home. Be realistic and know the limitations of what your care home can achieve, what debt levels it can service, what investment requirements are needed and what profitability and cash it can generate. Far too many care businesses fail because their owners get the fundamentals wrong or they themselves get greedy.

Budget

"Turnover is vanity, profit is sanity". Never a truer word has been spoken. Budget realistically and truthfully, even if the result you come up with is not what you want. While every business needs turnover, it is the profit you generate from that turnover which is the most important. Make sure your budget tells you what you can make from your care home, and if it's not what you want it to say then take action in a thought-through manner.

Control

Stay in control of your care home. If you let other people take control, whether that's in care delivery or how your care home is managed generally, then trouble will follow. Of course you can't do everything yourself, but only delegate your work when you have the confidence you know you can, and only when you have confidence in the person to whom you have delegated.

Compare

What did your care home manage to achieve last year? Can you go one better the following year or, perish the thought, is your care home's performance deteriorating? If the latter, then with good accurate information you should be able to quickly identify the problem and have time to take swift corrective action.

Analyse

If a category of income or cost is not what you have budgeted for, then analyse it thoroughly and find out where the discrepancy lies. It could be occupancy, it could be the average fee, it could be the staffing rota, maybe you have incurred too much on agency staff or simply the food costs or energy costs are rising. But know where the problem lays and do something about it to correct it before it gets out of control.

Challenge

Challeng your staff, your commissioners, your regulators – as long as you are confident that you know what you are talking about! You may not win every argument, but equally you won't lose every one either. Don't accept something simply because 'that's how it's always been done'. Often increased revenues or decreased costs come from challenging what is perceived as 'normal'.

Monitor

Follow your care home's key management performance indicators with real tenacity. Good accurate weekly performance data can often tell you much more about the current health of your business than waiting for the end of the month accounts to be produced.

Review

Always take time to review the performance of the people who work in your care home, *because they are your business*. Don't ever become complacent, because complacency will breed failure, and failure will cost you your reputation, and loss of reputation will cost you money.

"You will never get a 6 unless you roll the dice."＊

Bring solutions

'Bring me solutions to the problem, not the problem itself'. Far too many people only react once the problem is brought to them. Good care home managers should also be good business managers who in turn have good people working for them. *Expect* to be told the solution to the problem, not always have the problem brought to you to solve. Only by asking "what action have you taken" will people start to understand that managing a care home in a competent and financially astute way is not easy.

Timeliness

Out-of-date information is no use whatsoever. What use are monthly accounts that are two months late or service delivery information that is several months late? The information upon which you make your decision has to be produced in a timely manner. If it isn't then it's not worth the paper it's written on or the time spent reading it.

＊ *This should, though, NOT be taken in the context that risk-taking is good or is the sole driver of business success – on the contrary. This quote was made by a 'failed' entrepreneur called Reuben Singh, who subsequently was declared bankrupt. In my eyes it epitomises much of what became of the health sector in the early to mid-2000s, in that there was far too much risk-taking (almost on the roll of a dice), as opposed to sound business planning and management decision making. Too many people think it's good to take risks in business, and well thought-through, calculated risk-taking often can lead to success, but don't leave anything to just 'chance' because the chances of throwing a 6 every time are very small.*

Accounting demystified: issues managers cannot afford to ignore

ANDREW BROOKES

has specialised in advising operators for 20 years, focusing on accounting, tax planning, acquisitions and disposals, and is recognised for advising the sector.

Accounts and financial information can be a bit of a mystery, for which John Cleese has a lot to answer for! It is actually not as difficult as it might seem. It is all about breaking it down into bite-size chunks while using plain English, without jargon and technical speak. In the following paragraphs I aim to demystify the interpretation of accounts and help you understand what the key performance measures are and how you can influence or improve these. Any improvement not only increases profits each year, but will also enhance the capital value of the business.

What is a profit and loss account?

The profit and loss account is the record of income and expenses and, therefore, profit for a period. It is the measure of financial performance and influences how much the business might be worth. Paying attention to it is really important.

What is a balance sheet?

The balance sheet is a record of all the assets and liabilities of a business. Assets include fixed assets (buildings/furniture, etc.), debtors and cash. Liabilities include creditors, tax, bank loans, etc. It can have an impact on the value of the business and you can influence this with thought.

Occupancy and fee rates

The biggest number in your accounts will be fee income, which is the driver to pretty well everything. If you increase fees by only £10 per week, it makes an enormous difference. £10/week for 30 service users would increase annual profit by £15,000 and the value by a multiple of this.

Controlling staff costs

Staff costs will be your largest outgoing. You should monitor establishment hours, handover periods, sick leave, agency usage versus bank staff, and control the costs. Ten hours of agency staff per week could reduce annual profits by £2,000 and the business value by a multiple of this.

Retain good staff

A key to delivering high quality care and controlling staff costs is good stable staffing. Have you evaluated the cost of recruiting new staff? It may cost more to advertise, interview, obtain Disclosure and Barring Service (DBS) checks, provide training, etc. than to pay existing staff a little bit more.

Look after overheads

By controlling overheads, it may be possible to spend the savings on enhancing the service provided, making the home more attractive to residents. We work with many clients, benchmarking costs against those for the sector, to help identify possible savings. We then help them negotiate better supply contracts.

Valuing your business

Everything so far in this section has focused on profit. Earnings (profit) before Interest, Tax, Depreciation and Amortisation (EBITDA) typically forms the basis of valuing a care business. An increase in EBITDA could have a dramatic effect on the capital value of your business, this is why it is key.

Tax planning

Taking good tax advice is a critical part of running any business, with different rates for personal and corporate taxes. It is important to make sure you plan your affairs in the most tax efficient way. This is frequently not properly considered and we can nearly always reduce tax bills.

Case History

A home owner came to us hoping to sell their home for "a significant sum", having made only £250,000 profit in the previous financial year. With careful planning, a review of costs and structure of the business, we helped over the next two years to increase profits to £450,000 and make it achievable.

The value of good accounting records

Some might see accounts as a necessary evil! It is, however, essential in a changing market, to know both the cost of care and the "hotel" costs. On sale of your business, your accounts will be subject to scrutiny and quality records should help you achieve more on sale.

Planning the future of the business

It is important to plan for the future and to ensure that the home has longevity. Plan expenditure to keep the home future-proof, attractive and welcoming. Look at marketing carefully and ensure the care home's website is fresh and shows the home well, while making sure that you rank well on Google searches.

Making your bank happy: key points for managers

PAUL BIRLEY

is head of public sector & healthcare, Barclays. "Our aim is to give people in care a better experience by providing financial support to those operators delivering great care."

Some might presume that the secret to keeping your bank happy is a strong financial performance. This is, of course, important but there's something far more fundamental which forms the essence of a good relationship – the delivery of great care. Banks aren't experts in running care homes but we have a desire to support the aspirations of those operators delivering great care, and a strong understanding of the challenges facing the sector. This enables us to provide much needed support and deliver banking solutions designed to help operators grow. When care is delivered well – homes can be inspirational places and it's these operators we look to support.

People before profits

The resident must be the focus for all care home operators. If, in conversation with us, an owner raises the profitability of the home ahead of the welfare of its residents, it's probably not a home we'd look to support. People should always come before profits.

No substitute for a visit to the care home

There's no substitute for visiting homes.Valuations and inspection reports are important but you can't get a full understanding of a home without visiting it yourself. The homes I like to visit are those furthest away from an operator's head office where senior management's influence is likely to be diluted by distance. When I was a junior bank manager we were sent on a course on how to be good managers. The lecturer said he'd written down the answer under our seats. We all got up – only to find there was nothing there. That was the lesson – get up and go and see your clients.

First impressions count

When you visit a home you can quickly tell whether it's well run. The external look of the home, the welcome from staff, the demeanour and well- being of the residents – all give a good impression of the rest of the home. Look in the linen cupboard – if it's a mess the home is probably a mess, if it's neat and tidy, it's probably not used. I like a linen cupboard that's slightly ruffled – well used but organised. I also like to look in the fridge for fresh produce or check the quality of the doors and beds – all tell-tale signs of a good home.

Watch the cash

Businesses can quickly get into difficulty if cash gets stretched, therefore operators should watch the cash all the time. A number of operators who bank with us keep enough cash readily available to cover one month's expenses, just in case.

Borrow within your means

Don't borrow more than you can afford. Ambition is a great attribute but, don't push it. Some of the most successful operators have been those which set out a strategy and stuck to it.

Management information

Have comprehensive management information (MI): If you don't know how you're performing how can you make decisions about the future? When we look back at businesses which got into difficulty – a common trait was a lack of decent MI.

Keep it simple

If it's too complex – it probably is.

"A deep knowledge of the sector and understanding of the issues facing operators. Good relationships with major players and keen supporter of the sector."

– JUDGES' COMMENT, HEALTHINVESTOR AWARDS 2012

Good management is key

A poor home can be run by good management although it won't stay poor for long. However, poor management cannot run a good business for very long before it fails.

Attention to detail

Running a care home is complex and challenging with increasing compliance – therefore it's crucial that all the detail is correct. Dot the Is, cross the Ts and then underline them and you're probably halfway there.

Communication

Successful operators know the value of effective communication and have developed good relationships with their stakeholders – including residents, staff, commissioners, local authorities, regulators, inspectors and relatives.

Making the most of your GP

DR GILLIE EVANS

is a GP principal, founder member of Peterborough Palliative Care in Dementia Group, and RESEC Associate Fellow, Green Templeton College, Oxford researching relationships between GPs and care homes.

As a GP, I look after the residents of a 55-bed specialist nursing home, all of whom have dementia. I have visited the home weekly for more than 12 years and built up good and mutually supportive working relationships with the staff. At monthly multidisciplinary significant event meetings we have discussed all aspects of the care provided for residents and worked together to improve communication, resolve problems, identify and meet training needs and develop practical tools. It is this experience which underpins the points below. If you have multiple visiting GP practices, focus attention on the best one or two.

Build a good working relationship

Identify the GP from the practice(s) looking after your residents who shows greatest interest and involvement. Suggest a discussion to review and resolve the problems that arise, from both your perspectives, when residents need visiting. Offer a named, fully briefed, supernumerary member of staff to support the GP during visits.

Highlight the benefits of a regular 'ward round'

Encourage the GP to identify a regular weekly visit time which avoids mealtimes. Suggest the GP asks his/her practice for protected time; minor problems, new residents, chronic disease and medication reviews and availability for relatives can usually wait for the "ward round" and overall visit requests will be reduced.

Provide a private room for discussion

Care homes rarely have consulting rooms. Too often residents are discussed and reviewed in public areas. Identify a room for the regular GP visit for confidential discussions and review of ambulant residents as required (eg hairdressing room, relatives' room). Ensure residents needing more extensive examination are in their own rooms.

Facilitate access to clinical notes

Where possible, make sure the GP knows in advance which residents are for review so notes are available. Discuss how best to keep clinical information held in the home up-to-date. Consider a secure link to the practice computer via a dedicated phone line to allow clinical record access.

Anticipate requirements in acute illness

Visit requests for acute infections are common. The GP will need to know if the resident is eating, behaving normally (especially in dementia), has reduced mobility, increased confusion, has a temperature and what is in the urine. If chest /skin examination is required, the resident should be in his/her own room.

Medication: aim to improve prescribing and safety

Highlight residents on large numbers of drugs, (more than six), for quarterly review. Clarify the rationale for every drug and suggest explanatory prescribing instructions, e.g. "one daily to lower blood pressure". Agree who informs the dispensing pharmacist of changes. Suggest significant event review of medication errors with the GP to improve safety.

Make the GP aware of routinely collected data for the benefit of residents

Many care homes weigh residents and check blood pressures monthly. Don't record consistently low blood pressures, (lower than 125/70), without requesting review. Reducing medication could result in marked improvement in mobility and wellbeing. Alert the GP to progressive weight loss in a resident for which there may be a remediable cause.

Case History

"No potential for rehabilitation."

A 90-year-old resident with vascular dementia. Minimally responsive, weight 39.5kg, hoisted for transfers, twice weekly enemas, Bartel score ADL 8. Analgesia for OA knees, movicol for bowels. Encouraged to eat.

12 months later: walking with two people, Bartel score ADL 54, weight 57.4kg, eating well, recognises family, wonderful smile.

Share communication with relatives

For larger homes, GPs won't have time to see all relatives; it helps to know that staff routinely update relatives after GP visits. When there are problems with particular relatives or they have anxieties, tell the GP and ask for his/her support. Encourage relatives to attend the regular 'ward round'.

Encourage a proactive approach to medical care

Take the lead and encourage the GP in advance care planning and Do Not Attempt Resuscitation decisions. Some GPs will be reluctant to address this with residents and relatives and your experience will help them gain confidence. Discuss prevention of emergency admissions and review any that occur with the GP.

Share a commitment to care for residents to the end of life

Develop a shared resolve with the GP to ensure residents die peacefully and with dignity in the care home if at all possible. Encourage regular discussion about those residents thought to be close to the end of life and anticipate the likely medical needs. Review lessons learnt after each death.

Preparing your care home for an inspection

KAREN ROGERS

is the owner of an expanding group of fully compliant care homes in Herefordshire. She was previously a care home inspector and manager of an inspection team. Karen has had numerous articles published and has a mission to show that care homes can be a fantastic place to live.

Inspection is more than a regulator confirming compliance; it's a powerful marketing tool that, in conjunction with other indicators, informs prospective residents, commissioners and other stakeholders about the quality of the service being provided. It is therefore not surprising that managers find the experience quite stressful as a poor inspection will not only result in follow-up inspections visits but could also damage the reputation of the home. Having an effective quality management system in place that is known and understood by all staff is the key to having confidence that your care home will be compliant at any time should the inspector visit.

Purchase a copy of current legislation including regulations and standards

This will tell you what the law says you must do to be compliant, it will also tell you how to achieve compliance and what sanctions would be imposed for non compliance.

Know if your home is compliant or not!

The first stage in preparing for an inspection is to implement a quality management system that includes a continual programme of auditing. This will confirm compliance or what should be done to achieve compliance and will give the inspector confidence in the home's management. It is essential that the quality management system is part of the culture in the home, preventing the onus of compliance being the sole responsibility of the registered manager.

Observation

Take a tour of the home starting with the exterior. What will the inspector see when they pull up outside the home? Walk through the home; try to look at it with a fresh pair of eyes. What is the atmosphere like, how does it sound? Observe how staff interact with residents, do they obtain consent before carrying out tasks? Do residents appear well cared for?

Know which areas will be inspected

Review the previous inspection report to determine the standards most likely to be inspected. However, care planning, nutrition, auditing of accidents together with recruitment, induction and supervision are likely to be reviewed.

Be organised and delegate

Have a well-organised office. This will also help in the auditing process; an efficient well-organised office and manager who can instantly access records will project the impression of a well managed home.

Customer feedback

Regularly seek the views of people using your service, together with their relatives and other stakeholders. This can be done through meetings and surveys. These surveys must be acted upon to demonstrate that you listen to what people say.

Be confident

If you have followed the above you can be confident that the inspection will go well. If something unforeseen does happen on the day, the inspector will have confidence that systems are in place to address any concerns.

"Our mission statement about treating people with respect and dignity is not just words but a creed we live by every day. You cannot expect your employees to exceed the expectation of customers if you don't exceed the employees' expectations of management."

– HOWARD SCHULTZ, CHIEF EXECUTIVE, STARBUCKS COFFEE

Know your risk rating

Inspectors monitor information about your service, collating information received from a number of sources including: notifications, safeguarding alerts, complaints, contract monitoring, pharmacy inspections, members of the public and Health Watch reviews.

Emphasise the positives!

The inspector will have a plan but you can focus on the positive aspects of the home and what has improved since the last inspection. Keep a list of achievements and development in the service. An inspector can only base their findings on what they see, read or are told during the inspection.

Feedback session

This is an opportunity to rectify any issues, or clear up misunderstandings that may have occurred during the inspection. If there is a possibility of non-compliance have a professional discussion and ask for evidence to support the inspector's conclusion, don't be afraid to challenge something if you disagree.

Getting it right on inspections

DAVID FRANCIS

is assistant chief inspector CSSIW, previously with CQC and CSCI. Lesley Hobbs is manager of Deerhurst Nursing Home providing dementia care near Bristol.

If you truly run a good service you should be confident! You can't fake it! Like most things in life, it's groundwork that counts. A good service puts the people it cares for first, fosters staff wellbeing and gets the basics right. A good service is always looking to learn and improve and sees inspections as a chance to get constructive, critical feedback and importantly know where its risks are– like MoTs help you to know if your car is safe. Get your line manager, if you have one, to see inspections in the same light. It will reduce the risk of you being piggy-in-the-middle. So rule one: having a positive, non-defensive attitude to inspections is essential.

Upstream

Inspections start a long time before any door is knocked-on. Inspectors review evidence and form an initial opinion beforehand. You have an opportunity to set the agenda by returning solid self-assessment. Demonstrate that people are at the centre of your service, that you have a handle on quality assurance, that people are consulted and that you are learning from incidents. Highlight ongoing improvements. Build a relationship throughout the year – keep inspectors informed of any issues, ask advice – be open and honest. Share success stories as well as not so good ones.

Greetings

Take time to understand what the inspector needs and be helpful. Explain your routine, any issues they need to be aware of and agree a plan, especially around receiving feedback. Forewarn the inspector about hot issues and avoid them having nasty surprises.

Demeanour

Be friendly and relaxed – inspectors are just doing a job. We are all working for the same purpose. If you know your service has failings then have a plan in place of how you intend to address them.

Give the inspector space

Don't crowd them or try to control them. Get a resident or junior member of staff to show inspectors around. This displays confidence.

Prepare

Managers know what is expected. Keep a file throughout the year with evidence of what inspectors want to see, e.g. supervision matrix, training spreadsheets, master staffing roster, property maintenance & annual checks. Keep all documentation within easy access – it avoids you getting flustered if you can't find it.

Care plans

Poor care plans are a common cause of failure on inspections. They should be person-centred, accurate and up-to-date. Regularly monitor care plans so there are no shocks on the day. Help staff to find ways to do them, create slack such as 'special days' where one person's care is reviewed.

Know your residents

Know their interests, life histories and also those of relatives so that they feel valued and will say so to inspectors when asked.

When you're not there

On your days off ensure that staff know what is expected and have access to the evidence file. If possible attend the inspection, it takes pressure of staff who's main concern should be care of residents, not chasing round for evidence and chaperoning inspectors.

"I never found inspections stressful because I worked hard to ensure we did our best to improve the lives of the people living with us and that's what inspectors want to find. See inspections as opportunities to learn and develop. If you have a vision, an inspection is your chance to shout about it."

– LESLEY HOBBS, MANAGER, DEERHURST

Familiarise staff

Ensure staff are used to people observing them at work. Observe them yourself, ask clinical leads, managers from other homes or directors. This way staff will carry on normally and won't hide away during inspections. It avoids the communal areas looking abandoned and residents appearing neglected. Offer praise and inspire confidence so staff feel confident that they can be themselves.

Feedback

Keep a note of feedback. Where things are unclear, ask. Where you disagree clarify the evidence. Welcome suggestions and remain positive.

Thanks to Lesley Hobbs for many of these suggestions!

Helping your residents to find funding

Finance is often a major concern for the families of those entering private care. With the cost potentially running into hundreds of thousands of pounds, ensuring there's enough money to meet the bills can be a real source of anxiety. Unfortunately, for many people the sums don't add up and around one in four self-funders find themselves running out of money while in care*. Although the state might step in, the resident risks losing control and choice over their care. To prevent this from happening families should be encouraged to access expert financial advice. A care fees professional; a specialist trained to advise on funding of care, and prevention of wealth depletion, may be the best solution.

Local Government Information Unit - Independent Ageing, 2011

KATE WAKEFIELD

works for PayingForCare – supporting care homes to implement processes to ensure that their self-funding residents and families have access to appropriate financial advice to prevent future wealth depletion. She is a qualified nurse and has worked in the private healthcare sector in various commercial roles for more than 25 years.

Give reassurance that most people find the care funding system complex

Navigating the care funding system is not easy, especially when most people have never had to do it before. With a mixture of means-tested benefits, funding based on health, and benefits that everyone can receive, it can be difficult to understand a resident's entitlement.

Discuss finances as part of your admission process

Residents' financial arrangements should be as much part of your formal admission process as obtaining the names of their GPs. A resident's financial welfare is an integral part of their health and wellbeing. Helping them understand how to secure this financial wellbeing will deliver the peace of mind to enable them and their families to relax and enjoy life.

Gently outline the implications of running out of money

Running out of money can be disastrous for residents and care homes. There is no guarantee that residents will continue to be funded by the state, in the home of their choice, once their money runs out. Explaining the implications at the earliest possible stage and helping them access financial advice will help to avoid this.

Ensure a Power of Attorney is in place

A Lasting Power of Attorney is essential. This ensures that a trusted person, for instance a member of the family or a close friend, can manage the resident's finances on their behalf if they are unable to do so themselves.

Encourage residents to seek professional help

Assessing a resident's finances yourself can be a futile exercise as there's often no guarantee the money is actually available or that it will last. To achieve better outcomes for everyone, it is better to direct them towards professional financial advice.

78

Don't just advise residents to 'seek advice'

Most people only deal with the financial aspects of paying for care once or twice in their lives so they're unlikely to know where to turn for expert advice. It is important to maintain impartiality and ensure that families have choice .Specialist, not-for-profit organisations are probably their best option.

Regularly revisit the financial arrangements

Circumstances change, and a resident's health can improve so dramatically once they have settled into the home that their life expectancy extends considerably, with significant financial implications. A six monthly review may be needed. Leaflets, articles in newsletters, information wih invoices and inviting speakers into the home can all help to raise awareness.

"Finding your way round the care funding system can be a pretty daunting task - it's complicated and something about which most of us have little or no knowledge."

Understand the implications of the Care and Support Bill

Although the Care and Support Bill aims to make care funding fairer, it also introduces greater complexity. In particular the cap on care costs has caused confusion, with many consumers mistakenly believing that once they have spent £72,000 on care the local authority will pick up the cost.

Learn to identify early signs of financial difficulties

Identifying potential problems early can enable you to provide much needed support by directing them towards financial advice. Warning signs can include late payment of fees and fewer visits to the home.

Should a resident's finances fail...

Some companies continue to support a resident whose finances have failed. Should yours not be one of those companies, then ensure that you first explore all the available options such as moving to an alternative room or top-ups from a family member. If there is no solution then work with the family to identify a suitable alternative provider, get the local authority involved as soon as possible and ensure that the transition process is as easy and painless as it can be.

Enabling your residents to live fulfilled lives in every sense

ROGER DAVIES

became chief executive of Methodist Homes (MHA) in 2001 and is a founder board member of the English Community Care Association (ECCA), Your Care Rating and the Association of Retirement Community Operators (ARCO).

Compassionate care and respect for each individual, inspired by Christian concern, has informed all MHA's developments and initiatives. We treat others, especially the most frail and vulnerable, with the dignity we wish for ourselves. Supporting older people to live a meaningful life involves nurturing their mind and spirit as well as their physical needs. It requires offering choices in all aspects of daily life; and creating special, personal experiences, for example through reflexology, which MHA has promoted in all its homes. By paying attention to the details, an individual's sense of well-being may be sustained.

Knowing each individual

Residents can be supported to make the most of life if staff members take the time to get to know about a person's past: where they came from, what their passions are. This helps build good relationships and understanding, not least with individuals living with memory loss, for whom music therapy has also proved able to help many individuals express themselves wonderfully.

Meeting spiritual needs

Spiritual well-being is not an optional add-on, which is why there is a chaplain in every MHA home. Older people desire the freedom to discover purpose and meaning in life, which may be found in many ways: from practising formal religious beliefs to enjoying the outdoors or building friendships.

Making homes into 'homes'

Retaining one's own sense of personality underpins a fulfilled life. For example: choosing the décor of one's room as well as taking into it one's own belongings; or feeling that members of staff have time for you as a person. From such details, a residence can become a loved home.

Drawing on local people and resources

Developing a team of volunteers who are part of the life of a home is enormously supportive for staff members and residents alike. Four thousand volunteers are key to enhancing MHA's charitable services. They help bring the surrounding community directly to residents. So do visits by entertainers, Pets as Therapy dogs, or even a donkey!

Creating opportunities

Hopes and ambitions need not disappear with age. Enabling individuals to fulfil dreams – from visiting an old haunt to taking a first sky-dive – creates great joy, while marking birthdays or national events, organising trips and celebratory meals, all help individuals to feel part of the world around them.

Creating privacy in community

Flexible care allows individuals to choose how and where they spend their time. Few people wish to engage in group activities all the time; the value of having one's own front door shouldn't be underestimated. Personal space offers time for reflection, the reclaiming of individuality, and the re-charging of batteries.

Encouraging joy in eating

This most fundamental of daily routines can also bring pleasure. Varied menu choices; recipes that cater for individual needs; tables that are laid with care and attention to detail; and even the possibility of eating breakfast at a time that suits personal routines... Such options imply respect for personal taste.

Getting outside

The development of imaginative and sensory gardens has become the norm in MHA homes. Gardens with interesting, safe paths and raised flower beds can be accessed by wheelchair users and those living with dementia. Helping residents to share in the gardening or enjoy local wildlife can be a great source of fulfilment.

"Before I came here I had become ill and depressed but here the care is so good and we have so many activities. There's such a wonderful atmosphere. I don't know what would have happened to me had I not found this lovely home. I feel secure here."

– MHA RESIDENT

Welcoming partners and family

Helping couples to remain together when one partner needs greater care (for example following the onset of dementia) is a key MHA aspiration, which respects our fundamental desire for relationships. Indeed, relatives are welcomed as family in all our homes.

Supporting a good end

MHA's 'Final Lap' scheme has helped all care staff members to receive training in appropriate ways of helping residents, relatives and staff alike to face death openly and positively. All other residents are helped to prepare for an imminent loss, and end of life care is of the highest quality.

Making your care home person-centred

PROFESSOR DAWN BROOKER

is the director of the University of Worcester Association for Dementia Studies; a team making a positive difference to those living with dementia.

People need warm human relationships, particularly when they feel frail or confused. Person-centred care is the short hand for making this happen. The following are guiding principles for our interactions:
– How might this person interpret my behaviour?
– Does my behaviour show that I respect, value, and honour this person?
– Am I helping this person feel they are special?
– Am I helping this person to feel confident and that they are not alone?
It is not the task that is person-centred but the way in which that task is done that makes it person-centred or not.

Don't become immune to feelings

A lot of so-called "behaviour problems" occur because care is not person-centred. Although cognitive abilities may decline, there is no decline in depth of feeling or the range of emotions that people experience. Anxiety, fear, shame, grief, loneliness, boredom and anger are often the emotional undercurrent for residents in care. In our busyness it's easy for this to be overlooked or for staff to become immune to this. We sometimes don't see that a TV turned up too loud is scaring a resident or that standing over someone having a laugh and a joke is intimidating.

Warmth and respect

With the onset of dementia, individuals are very vulnerable to their sense of self being broken down. As verbal abilities are lost, warm human contact becomes even more important. Courtesy, respect, friendliness and kindness are communicated powerfully by non-verbal actions and tone of voice.

Use it or lose it

Activity and engagement with residents is integral to care work, not an added extra. Worthwhile activity and engagement defined as what is meaningful to residents, not pre-determined.

The culture of compassion

The aim is to ensure that person-centredness become the norm for everyone; that our culture of care is person-centred. Make no mistake, culture of care is powerful. How managers conduct themselves with staff has a direct bearing on how staff conduct themselves with residents and families.

Model the principles

Managers should never to forget this. If they actively model the above principles on a day-to-day basis, and use language that gives people status rather than demeans them, then there is a good chance that staff and visitors will follow their lead. In leading by good eample the chances are that everyone else's care will follow suit.

Person-centredness applies to staff as well

Person-centredness is not just how staff are with residents. If managers apply person-centred principles with staff, then they will be more likely to put these into practice with residents. We have lots of evidence to show that when the personhood of staff is respected then they will respect the personhood of residents.

Staff morale

High levels of staff turnover, staff shortages and poorly trained staff lead to negative quality of life for care-home residents. Staff who feel demoralised, burnt out and stressed are unlikely to be able to take the care to communicate in the respectful, warm and inclusive way that is required in person-centred care.

"As we become more emotional and less cognitive, it's the way you talk to us, not what you say, that we will remember... Your smile, your laugh and your touch are what we will connect with. Empathy heals. Just love us as we are. We're still here, in emotion and spirit, if only you could find us."

– CHRISTINE BRYDEN, 2005

Build a sense of friendship

Make sure everyone involved in the care home knows they matter and that they are special. This includes the youngest and the oldest, the fittest and the most frail and the noisiest and the quietest. This applies to residents, staff and visitors.

Embrace change

People and organisations change all the time. Be open to change for the benefit of residents. What works today may not work tomorrow.

Don't let the pressure get to you

Managers are often overburdened with many external pressures that make it hard to be person-centred. Try not to let these pressures influence how you are with staff and residents. Be forgiving of yourself and others.

Making your care home dementia-aware

SHEENA WYLLIE

is director of dementia services for Barchester Healthcare.
"Working with people for the past 30 plus years is a privilege. My nursing roles have been in the NHS and the independent sector."

The importance of being dementia-aware cannot be understated. The work of organisations such as the Alzheimer's Society in raising the profile of dementia and keeping this high on the political agenda has done much to support awareness in care homes. The 10 points below consider how to enable going beyond awareness, so that real change and meaningful lives are evident. To enable aspiration/vision to become a reality, facilitative leadership and tenacity is necessary. This is especially true when the vision challenges the comfortable status-quo of mediocrity. Changing the culture in your home is rewarding but, as Ghandi said: "You must be all the changes you want to make in the world".

Be dementia-aware

Being dementia-aware is not about separating the diagnosis from the essence of the person. Awareness is a key element for providing person-centred, holistic support. Keep the 'person' at the heart of everything.

Be fresh-eyed and brave

Most people will know when a care setting doesn't feel right and the culture of the home is merely rhetoric. Bravery is required to change that culture. Don't be afraid of commissioning external 'fresh eyes' to support the vision.

Be a believer

Read widely on person/relationship-centred approaches. Being person-centred is not just about dementia – getting the culture 'right' across the whole home will enhance everyone's lived experience. The 'magic' will come when it is translated into practice and enables staff teams to support people to live well rather than just exist.

Be bold

Don't ignore dementia – it is present. Dementia needs embracing, understanding and loving. Boldness is needed to introduce this concept to your management team, especially when changing culture and environments. While corporate and personal preferences need to be considered – these shouldn't override the real purpose of creating a meaningful and homely environment.

Be a role model and work in harmony with others

Share the vision with the people living in your home, their families and your staff team – and keep sharing it. You will need them to understand and participate in the changes that will need to take place for a whole home care culture. You will need to 'model' this approach – this means being it and not just doing it.

Be tenacious

It is perfectly reasonable to be unreasonable in periods of great change. You will need to be steadfastly focused on your vision. The pace of change needs to be noticeable, but not overwhelming for the team. You will also need to be prepared to lose some team members who are just not able to embrace a person-centred way of being.

Be creative

Choosing the right mix of skills and personalities to support a dementia-specific community requires considerable creativity in the selection process. Qualifications are not always the best indicator that someone has the 'heart' to care. Include the people living in your home in the selection and interviewing process.

Be mindful and create a continuous learning culture

The dementia diagnosis is important, but how this may affect the individual and their relationship with the world is even more so. There is always more to learn about the person and their needs. You may also have to step out of the accepted way of delivering care in order to support an individual –for example by wearing nightclothes as a cue to residents to persuade them to go to bed because you appear to be about to.

"Whatever you can do or dream, you can do, begin it. Boldness has a genius, and a power and magic in it. Begin it now."

– Goethe

Be nurturing

Recognise the team as people too. Caring is both emotionally rewarding and demanding. Asking people to deliver high quality person-centred care and support for 12 hours at the emotional level required is a *big* ask. Encourage the team to get to know each other – share life stories and be willing to share yours. Be visible and participative.

Be truthful

Be truthful with yourself and where you are positioned in delivering person-centred care. You will need to get rid of the old negative culture of care, but just layering person-centred care approaches at a senior level will not be enough. Recognise the reality and the 'truth' about life in your care home. This truth needs to be the experience of the people who are living there. An audit tool to support your findings will be invaluable when sharing the truth with the team. This will offer immense insight into how our actions or inactions impact on the lives of people living in a care home. Enabling team and family members to participate is a powerful way for the truth to be seen, felt and heard.

Last words: "Have fun."

Accepting that homes have front doors while institutions have 'units'

DR DAVID SHEARD

is founder/chief executive of Dementia Care Matters providing university recognised learning, developing Butterfly care homes and creating Feelings Matter Most training resources.

The feeling of being 'at home' in a house is well known to most of us. Yet dementia care 'units' proliferate the UK and Ireland. These units exist not only in name but in beliefs behind their models of care. Transferring what 'being at home' means into care home design and care home cultures still seems contentious. In the USA the 'Household Model' has been pioneered by LaVrene Norton, Action Pact and Steve Shields. This model identifies three components that support a home - renewal of the spirit, reframing the organisation and renovating into home. Similarly, Dementia Care Matters, in its Butterfly care home model, turns 10 key household beliefs into action:

A home needs the right name

A unit is industrial, a wing aristocratic, a suite superior, a facility faceless. Our struggle to name the parts of a care home represents our own confusion. Is a whole care home really a home and if so what is each part? The answer is a care home needs to be split into houses.

A house needs a front door

A unit represents a fragmented clinical area. Units, like hospital wards, tend to be accessed internally within the building through a pin coded door. Yet our own homes have a clear outside front door. Attaching a front door to each house in a care home is powerful – it requires a visitor to knock and to behave as a guest.

A home needs heart

A home thrives not on a person's work experience nor on their CV. A home has heart when the head of the home exudes spirit. Being open, real, loving and vulnerable demonstrates the human heart of a home. Recruiting a home manager with heart, prepared to share your life history with strangers, creates the feeling of 'home'.

A house needs a leader

A house needs co-ordination – most family homes have a leader. A day in a house involves observing people's quality of life, modelling real care and providing positive mealtime experiences – this needs a house leader. Presuming all nurses can instinctively lead is a mistake. People living and working together in a house need a natural, inspiring house leader to follow.

A home needs a housekeeper

A home provides warmth, comfort, relaxation, nourishment, and occupation. Splitting domestic, catering and cleaning functions into separate tasks delivered by separate people rips out the heart of a home. Employing a housekeeper or home maker who places people first and quietly sorts out tasks turns a facility into a home.

A house matches people together

A house works best with people who get on. Mixing up people in a house with very different needs often stresses people out. In a house, mixing up people living at different 'stages' of a dementia together creates an explosive brew. Different houses matched to people's different needs gives being person-centred a real chance.

A home brings out the best in people

A home recognises different strengths in people working there. No one individual can meet everyone's needs, nor is each person well matched to everyone. A home that matches people's special skills with people at a certain point of care will bring out the best in both people. Being person-centred to people involves reducing their need to keep switching their skills.

"Dividing care homes into houses with front doors, home makers and heart is the way to prove people really matter."

A house needs visiting partners

A house is lonely without visitors. Visiting a house can evoke different feelings. The degree of welcome, real involvement and feeling at home will influence whether we return. Visiting a care home without a role can feel faceless. A house that works gets families and friends involved in running the house and being a partner in the family house.

A home creates mutual regard

A home where people don't look after each other is a sterile house. Living together as separate islands is not a natural human state. A home that focuses on the quality of people's relationships stays glued together. A home that is full of disconnected people fractures. Seeing people living together, caring for one another, is proof of wellbeing.

A house needs wiring with emotional intelligence

A house full of people with skills and competencies doesn't make a home. A house turns into a home when people want to be together and 'get' each other. Being together involves growing acceptance of each other. Emotional intelligence is having the ability to reach out to people. Developing people's emotional intelligence is the primary competency to invest in.

New builds/extensions/refurbishments

Experience shows us that close collaboration and effective communication are essential ingredients for working successfully with your builder. Appointing a builder experienced in care home design and construction at the earliest possible stage and developing shared understanding and objectives with you and any other members of your professional team will facilitate this. These 10 'pearls of wisdom' will help guide you through your new build, extension or refurbishment process.

MELVILLE KNIGHT

is the group chief executive of Castleoak Group and has led the company into a £60 million development and construction organisation that specialises in care related projects.

Choose a builder that meets the basics

Make sure the builder registers your project with the Considerate Constructors Scheme (CCS) and takes health and safety seriously. The CCS ensures they will follow a best practice code of conduct. Also ask how health and safety compliance will be monitored.

Choose a builder with care home experience

There is no substitute for an experienced team with a good understanding of the workings of a modern busy care home. This is even more important when it comes to extensions and refurbishments: the planning and phasing of work safely around an operational care home presents major challenges.

Weigh-up costs and benefits

When budgeting for extensions and refurbishments, you should always allow for the additional cost of VAT (currently 20%). Often a replacement new build, which is zero VAT rated, is more cost-effective than a major extension refurbishment. The refurbishment of a home can be inefficient, lengthy and costly.

Check the design and specification before work starts

It's much easier and cheaper to change something on the drawing board than on site. This means it is essential to check the design and specification very carefully before work starts. Try and visualise what everything will look and feel like – for both residents and staff. Visits to recently completed schemes will help.

Plan the sequencing and logistics in detail

Careful and detailed advanced planning with your builder about the sequencing and logistics of the project is essential for success, especially for extensions and refurbishments. Look at the programme in detail and talk every aspect through, such as deliveries, parking, noise, storage and working hours.

Make sure design and cost are in sync

Be sure that design and cost estimating move forward at the same pace. This applies to change management as well as design development and ensures there are no conflicts or misunderstandings later down the line. Always ask in advance about the cost and time implication of any change that you wish to make.

Put residents and staff first

There is a fine balance between undertaking an extension or refurbishment as quickly as possible and respecting the interests of the residents and staff. The builder must bear in mind that the site is both a home and workplace – privacy, dignity and peace of mind for residents and staff should always come first.

Maintain good communication

Organise regular meetings to iron-out any problems or concerns and look ahead to the next week or planning period. Good communication is essential and face-to-face meetings are particularly helpful because they can help to build the relationship with your builder.

"Close collaboration and effective communication are essential ingredients for working successfully with your builder."

Involve residents and staff

Work with your builder to engage residents and staff. For example, can they get involved in choosing colour schemes or shrubs for the garden, or even naming the new home or an area within it? Put plans and photographs on display, along with details of the programme.

Plan for a smooth handover

Focus on the handover requirements. Be specific and work with your builder so you both know what to expect when the time comes to handover. Make sure they provide training on all new systems and equipment and provide 'as built' drawings and manuals.

Making the most of IT

Although generally Information Technology (IT) has not been used widely in care homes things have been changing over the past decade. Developments have been made in a number of areas including care home management, finances, the keeping of records, staff rostering and, more recently, in medication management, care planning and compliance. However, use of IT in these areas is far from universal. This chapter focuses on the benefits IT can bring to the care home and looks at the contribution it can make to the person-centred delivery of care.

NEIL BRYANT

is the managing director of MyAmego Healthcare, a specialist software and systems integration company. He is a keen advocate of using technology to enhance residents' independence and wellbeing, particularly those with long term conditions such as dementia and learning disabilities and in improving care delivery in care homes.

Managing the home

Computer systems can greatly enhance management record keeping and home compliance. Record keeping systems offer compact record storage and ease of access to information (even when archived), with compulsory fields helping ensure records contain uniform and complete information. Automatic prompts can send reminders about updates and reviews.

Safety

Nurse call systems (the staple requirement of CQC) have changed. Wireless systems offer greater flexibility; call points can be repositioned and compatible devices used for different, and changing, needs. Alerts can be sent discretely to staff pagers and reports on response times generated. Some systems passively monitor residents' risks and support least restrictive practice while safeguarding staff.

Enablement/reablement

IT can support occupation and activity, promoting maximum wellbeing of people, including those living with dementia. Choice is increasing, from software-based life histories, colour by numbers and music, to systems that give residents the chance to move around the home and its grounds without intrusive supervision.

Supporting staff

IT can support staff in daily tasks and minimise time off 'the floor'. Conveniently located PCs, laptops, tablets, pagers or phones enable carers to reduce unnecessary 'leg work' to a central office or nurse station; staff, continuing to be available to residents while automatic prompts support consistent and timely care delivery.

Communication

IT can enhance communication with health professionals and families; perhaps offering email updates or text prompts for medication or physiotherapy reviews or simply email or internet phone call updates to residents' families or from residents to their families, as part of the service.

Transparency

IT can help with the sharing of information, whether, for safeguarding, care enhancement or reassurance. Consider sharing aspects of care planning, or wellbeing information, such as mobility data, with other care professionals or residents' families, or with commissioners for care package review.

Care planning

I have singled this out becaue care planning is critical to care delivery and compliance. A computer-based care planning tool has great advantages; like other record keeping, it is space saving, accessible remotely and uniform across all records but can also generate emails and deliver prompts and reminders to update or review.

Ongoing assessment

Collecting information about residents' wellbeing and activity over time can help in assessing stages in a condition, how medication or physiotherapy for example, is impacting on people. It can also help in discussions with other care professionals and families and support proactive, rather than reactive, care delivery.

"The first rule of any technology used in a business is that automation applied to an efficient operation will magnify the efficiency. The second is that automation applied to an inefficient operation will magnify the inefficiency."

– BILL GATES

Person-centred care

IT can support both active and inactive residents' wellbeing and personal needs and preferences. This might be directly through activity and wellbeing information and via care prompts and reminders, or indirectly via management and staff benefits arising from computerised rostering or better care planning.

Image

A care home that embraces and publicises its effective use of various forms of IT shows a progressive business image. IT should be a tool to structure care home practices and a means of evidencing a well managed and proactive care home with enhanced resident opportunities.

Making the most of your outdoor space

ANNIE POLLOCK,
is director of landscape design, Dementia Services Development Centre, University of Stirling.

Sunshine helps my body make vitamin D, essential for my bones and my health; bright light maintains my circadian rhythm, helping me sleep at night; freedom for me is being able to go outdoors when I want to, through an unlocked door. Many people in care homes are denied this, even though being outdoors can improve their health, relieve stress and provide opportunities for either being alone or being sociable. Flowers and plants cheer me up, keeping me in touch with nature.

A safe secure place
If the outdoor environment isn't safe and secure, staff won't allow me to go outside alone. You need to be sure that I can't climb the fencing, 'escape' through a gate, or fall over the balustrade of a balcony or roof terrace.

Inconspicuous enclosure
To me, in the UK, conspicuous enclosure looks imprisoning, although I know that in other countries such as Australia, fencing means safety, keeping wild animals out! If you 'soften' the fencing with colour and planting, it will look so much better. The plants will stop me from reaching it too. I like it to look familiar, to look like what I remember when I was young.

A comfortable environment, access in all weathers
Being older, I do feel heat and cold. So the outdoors needs to give me shade and shelter to encourage me out even when the weather is inclement. 'Half way' spaces such as verandas and conservatories are useful for this – as I can sit there and look out. Outdoor canopies, pergolas and gazebos are useful too.

Attractive views, easy surveillance
Attractive views encourage me to go outdoors. Large, unobstructed windows allow me, sitting or standing, an unimpeded outlook. Also the staff can see me when I'm outside, making sure I'm safe.

Easy navigation in and out of the building
I sometimes need clues to find my way in and out. An unlocked door of a different colour/tone to adjoining windows, a visible and easy-to-use door handle and plenty of signs with lettering and a picture really help me. Waymarking with objects of memorabilia helps me too. It's nice to have a toilet nearby.

Appropriate surfacing

I need level, even, well-drained surfacing. If the colour or tone is similar to the indoor flooring and threshold, I won't mistake it for a step. Looking domestic helps me to feel comfortable walking on it. I don't much like black asphalt, it reminds me of a street or school playground. Raised edgings might trip me up.

A circular path with handrails and ramps

I like to walk round a gentle path when I'm outdoors, with signs to help me to find interesting things. Seats at regular intervals help me rest and views to the entrance help me find my way back indoors. I like the colour/tone of the path to be similar to the patio, so I am not confused by it.

Resting places and areas for retreat

Plenty of visible resting areas encourage people like me to go outdoors and walk. Having places of quiet and calm provide me with much needed areas of retreat from the hustle-bustle of the care home. I need seats that are robust, comfortable and have arms to help me get up and down.

"Just living is not enough... one must have sunshine, freedom, and a little flower."

– Hans Christian Andersen

Some familiar objects

I like to feel at home and familiar objects help with this, such as lines for hanging out clothes, garden sheds, greenhouses, allotments, objects from my youth, perhaps from my workplace. These trigger memories I had forgotten and help me to do everyday things.

Activities for all

I like to feel useful. Having things to do, places to go, activities to join in, encourage me and help to improve my health and my memory. I talk to other people. Outdoor lighting means I can be outdoors on summer evenings, when I can't sleep – enjoying the stars and the moon.

Making your care home environment dementia friendly

DAMIAN UTTON

is a partner at Pozzoni Architects, specialising in design for older people. He also writes and speaks on design for dementia and older people.

People with dementia can be more sensitive to the built environment and they may not remember or understand their surroundings. Dementia friendly environments can compensate for the challenges associated with dementia and with old age. Good design can improve the quality of life of people with dementia by enabling them to be more independent and by reducing agitation, confusion, restlessness and distress. In turn this can also reduce stress on staff and families. This is a brief overview, for more detail please refer to the design guides published by the Dementia Services Development Centre at the University of Stirling.

Compensating for impaired memory

Glass fronted cupboards and wardrobe doors; painting toilet doors in a contrasting colour and installing clear pictorial signs can help residents remember where things are. The sound and smell of food preparation can act as a memory trigger as these senses are as important as sight.

Compensating for impaired learning

Clear contrast between wall and floor junctions; doors, switches, support rails standing out from wall surfaces, upholstery contrasting with the floor can all help people with dementia to more easily understand their surroundings. A dark toilet seat that contrasts with white sanitaryware will make the toilet obvious. Contrast is more important than colour. A small raised button on a handrail provides a tactile cue to the end of the handrail.

Compensating for impaired reasoning

If locked doors match the surrounding wall finish, skirting boards and handrails are fixed across the door and handles changed to flush fittings this can overcome the frustration of residents trying to open a locked door. Corridor dead-ends can be confusing so create an 'event' with objects such as hatstand, rummage box, or table and chair.

Visuo-perceptual

People with dementia can misinterpret what they see. Patterns can be confusing, speckled worktops perceived as crumbs and shiny floor surfaces as wet. Plain, matt finishes to wall and floor finishes can reduce this confusion. A sharp contrast between floor surfaces can also be perceived as a step and a dark area of floor area as a hole. Similar flooring tones can overcome this.

Orientating and understandable

Using objects for orientation can help people with dementia to find their way around, e.g. the lounge door is next to the clock. Fittings and fixtures should be domestic and familiar in their appearance such as a flush handle toilet. Research has shown that people with dementia best remember the time from when they were in their 20s and 30s and décor and furnishings should reflect their age group.

Self-esteem

Helping people to find their bedroom door can be achieved with memory boxes, photos or other objects. Clothes hung on a rail or peg in the order they are put on can help residents to dress themselves with confidence. An accessible kitchen and space for everyday tasks provides opportunities for purposeful activity.

Ease of access

Residents should be able to find their way around without obstructions. Access to communal areas and gardens, individual bedrooms and toilets should be obvious with doors equipped with hold-open devices.

"Our residents might have dementia, but they're not stupid."

– Stephen Judd, chief executive, HammondCare, Australia

Light and sound

Sight impairment requires high lighting levels. Removing pelmets, tie back curtains from windows and prune trees if necessary. Consider higher wattage lightbulbs and additional lights. Sound absorbing carpets and soft furnishings can reduce confusing background noise.

Gardens

External space is as important as internal space. Colour and smell of gardens, comfortable, protected seating areas and views to the outside world provide stimulation. There are opportunities for purposeful activity with raised planters and vegetable patches.

Don't do it all at once!

Sudden changes can be confusing as residents may have difficulty in adjusting to change.

The 'night-life' in a care home should be fun and safe

When I moved to Eagle House in 1990, due to Sheffield's large psychiatric hospital closing down under the Community Care Act, I didn't need or intend to work nights but the day jobs were taken. With little experience of night work, I just ran the shifts much as I had on days. However, the out-dated attitudes among some staff surprised me. The move to care in the community had brought massive changes to the culture of care except, it seemed, on nights. It was very satisfying to work towards changing this, but maintaining these standards has needed vigilance.

JANET LEIGH

from Anchor's Eagle House, Sheffield, has worked in psychiatric care for 34 years, 22 of those on night shift. She won the Care Registered Nurse category in the National Care Awards in 2012.

A very good place to start

Some people have rigid personalities and will never understand such concepts as person-centred care and residents' dignity. As a third of the night staff, one person can really undermine the care given but time spent correcting them to no avail is time taken from the residents. Managers, please select staff who can respond to the training you will give them.

Safety first

With a tiny night team, residents' unstable health problems and competition for emergency services from the city's nightlife, we must be prepared. Train staff to learn all risk assessments, to report any worries and to tell you their whereabouts throughout the shift. Anticipate and plan for problems at handover, secure the home immediately and clear routine tasks as soon as possible.

.. and second!

Night team leaders should know policies and procedures thoroughly to avoid losing time in an emergency by checking them or phoning company help-lines. We should have the confidence to make decisions instead of waking managers, making them less fit for duty next day.

Them and us

Occasional negative attitudes towards night workers should be dealt with by good communication of what we do. We chose these hours so must deal with the challenges, mainly staying awake. Personal techniques can be planned in supervision to achieve this. Managers can ease the difficulties by extra health monitoring and careful planning of rotas and mandatory training sessions.

Think positive

Feeling "up against it" produces strong team bonds, a shared humour and a working style that supports everyone. If staff relate to residents as they do to each other, then residents can feel included in the happy atmosphere.

What do residents really want?

We must work to policies, but residents just want us to care enough about them to provide snacks, help them to bed, reassure them if confused or remembering past abuse, and socialise if they want to stay up. More than anything, those asleep need us to work quietly.

It's their choice

Poor sleep is both a symptom and cause of mental ill-health and is a night care priority, but some residents prefer the quiet and intimacy of the night hours to be with staff. We should find a balance and provide peaceful activities and company. Not forgetting New Year's Eve, of course!

"Every fairy take his gait,
And each several chamber bless,
Through this palace with sweet peace,
Ever shall in safety rest."

– WILLIAM SHAKESPEARE *"A MIDSUMMER NIGHT'S DREAM"*

Training not straining

If residents don't directly need us, we have the chance to train. We can help staff gain qualifications but should take care as computer screens and long periods of reading can cause eye-strain at night. Team leaders should be able to talk at length about most care issues that crop up. This won't hurt anyone's eyes, (their ears, maybe!).

Collective wisdom

Team leaders are responsible for producing effective care plans, but residents often disclose vital information to other staff. With more time on nights for brainstorming sessions, we can quickly produce good resident reviews. Just make sure each contributor gets credit from management.

... and when all's said and done

Sleepy morning smiles, from the residents because they have slept well and from the staff who are about to, mean it was a successful shift. Everything else is a bonus. Relax.

Working with a staff member who is underperforming

ANNE SMITH, *director of Brilliant Care Solutions, has a reputation as a successful director of operations, senior nurse and award winning project manager. She currently works with care providers improving occupancy, achieving compliance and securing better care outcomes for residents.*

It is natural to feel discomfort in managing staff underperformance because of potential conflict, but managed proactively and consistently it can provide a real opportunity for the employee to develop and the staff team and residents to benefit as a whole. A member of staff who is underperforming can have a very negative impact on their own career, the wider team's morale, the standard of care received by residents and the reputation of the manager. It is important that the correct procedures are followed but successful outcomes are frequently dependent on the manager's own abilities and behaviours.

Develop a culture of continuously improving performance

In the current climate it is more crucial than ever that a manager really values their staff team and gets the best out of every member; giving them responsibility and making them accountable right from the outset. Good performance management helps identify underperformance promptly and achieves better outcomes for everyone: residents, staff and the business.

Avoid labelling staff

Avoid terms like 'poor performer' because they can stigmatise the employee and reflect badly on the manager's ability to manage. Such terms suggest that not only is the employee a lost cause but that management has not got on top of the problem, perhaps even silently condoning the poor performance.

Act promptly and calmly

Act on conduct and performance issues as soon as they occur. Equally, it is important not to show anger and to take a measured approach, assessing the situation and planning for the desired outcomes before taking action.

Communicate effectively

Make sure the conversation with your staff member takes place without interruption in private. Your message needs to be honest and clear as to the transgression. Discussing the evidence and consequences will help clarify what the staff member has done and its effect on them, their colleagues and residents. The message must not be confused by additional information or indeed praise, and at the end it is helpful to check the staff member's understanding of the conversation and what will be happening next. For all but trivial issues it is usually advisable to have another senior staff member present to reassure and take notes.

Assess the gravity of the situation

Establish the severity and likely causes of the poor performance, including whether it is due to lack of ability or motivation. This will help determine how the poor performance should be managed. Poor conduct may need to go straight to disciplinary process after investigation whereas performance issues may not, once reasons such as absence of training or ill health are considered. Your company's HR policies are essential in helping your assessment.

Find a SMART solution

Where appropriate, the member of staff should be encouraged to propose their own solution as this helps ensure ownership. The solution should be recorded using a SMART framework, which is 'specific, measurable, achievable, realistic and timely'. Putting a date and time in the diary to review progress ensures follow-up happens.

Monitor and give feedback

An absence of monitoring can lead to slippage in performance. Once the SMART solution is agreed, it is very important to monitor and follow-up the staff member so that improved behaviours can be recognised and positively reinforced, while further transgressions are challenged and managed.

"The conventional definition of management is getting work done through people, but real management is developing people through work."

– Agha Hasan Abedi

The importance of HR policies

Good foundations such as clear, precise job descriptions and effective supervision and appraisal systems help avoid poor performance, while capability procedures minimise the possibility of a successful employment tribunal claim for discrimination or victimisation.

Keep to the process

From the start it is vital to keep to company procedure, to make it clear to the staff member what triggers the next stages, and then be prepared to move to more formal procedures if there is no improvement.

Support, not punish

Working with a staff member who is performing poorly is primarily about supporting and helping them to achieve and sustain the desired improvements in their performance. It may also be an opportunity for you to re-evaluate your own performance to decide whether you are providing the guidance and leadership the staff deserve.

Ideas for turning round a care home which is struggling but could be successful

RAVI GIDAR

is managing director of Gold Care Homes.

Most people think that running a care home is like running a hotel with permanent occupants. Little do these people know about the complexities of running a care home. The main challenge facing the care homes industry is making a profit while providing good quality care. Quality care is the foundation when dealing with struggling care homes. However, there are some good quality homes that do not make a profit. When asked about turning around struggling care homes, most people in the care homes industry talk about the lessons learnt from the failure of Southern Cross Healthcare. Southern Cross was a leasehold model with unsustainable rents. These rents led not only to lack of cash, but also to poor quality care. Transforming an unprofitable care home into a lucrative business requires a balance between income and costs. There are no short-cuts and no golden rule to improving performance. Below are some ideas that have proved successful in turning around a struggling care home:

Quality
Poor quality care will result in creating local authority blocks on referrals. A vicious cycle is created – reduced referrals leading to low occupancy causing a drop in revenue. The main focus has to be on contract monitoring and providing good quality service that is fully compliant and satisfies CQC.

Fee income/top line
Once the quality issues have been dealt with, the fee income needs to be addressed. With fixed costs, the care business can be simple. So, if the income is robust and the costs are at the right level, there should be a good gross profit.

Private and public funding ratio
This ratio is important because it impacts the average fee. If the cost of care exceeds the fee, then there is no cash surplus. I would expect the normal ratio to be about one third publicly-funded residents and two thirds self-funders. This varies greatly depending on region.

Staffing costs and agency usage
Agency usage has an important bearing on a care home's profitability. As agency staff can be 40% to 90% more costly than regular staff, more often than not use of agency staff diminishes profit. Getting the staffing costs to 50% of revenue in residential care and 60% in nursing care is the key.

Estate costs – décor and appearance

Enhancing the design and appearance of a care home is imperative. With a lack of interest and/or a lack of cash flow, the building becomes tired. Consequently, this sends the home on a downwards spiral, as a poor-looking, tired home does not attract residents, private or public.

Ethos and reputation

It takes time to build up the reputation of a care home. If the ethos of the home in the community has to be changed, a re-launch, an open day or a family event are examples of sure steps towards achieving the desired change.

Cash flow

Cash flow is important in any business. There can be several reasons for poor cash flow within a care homes business. Wrong invoicing and build-up of debt are the most common reasons for poor cash flow. Therefore, prompt debt collection is *vital* to improving cash flow. If cash flow is weak because of lack of sales, the problem may take longer to solve.

Leadership

Clear leadership is required to run a successful care home. Leadership starts with a competent home manager. Most struggling care homes do not have a manager or have the wrong person leading it. The owner provides the vision, but the clear leadership has to come from the home manager.

"It takes many good deeds to build a good reputation, and only one bad one to lose it."

– Benjamin Franklin

Category of care (e.g. residential, dementia)

The category of care could be an issue. Careful research needs to be done in order to ensure there is sufficient demand for the category of care that is offered. If the demand is not sufficiently high, the category of care may need to be changed. The classic example is changing residential care homes to dementia care homes. However, with more expenses, residential care homes can be changed to nursing care homes and vice-versa. Specialist care could also be considered.

Location and suitability

If the location of the care home is the reason why the care home is struggling, then the only solutions are to either use the building for alternative purposes or to redevelop it. If the location is suitable and there is demand, but the building is not fit for the purpose, flattening the building and building a purpose-built care home may be the best solution.

Managing complaints fairly and effectively

GILLIAN DALLEY

is a consultant with BCD Care Associates, researching and consulting on quality and standards in NHS and social care services for older people and was previously chief executive of the Relatives and Residents Association.

The aim of a complaints process in social care is to address concerns and seek resolution of distress, to the satisfaction wherever possible of all parties. A successful complaints process not only achieves these specific objectives fairly and effectively but also provides a care provider with the means of learning lessons from past mistakes and, in applying them, enables lasting improvements to services to be made.

Tell your customers and staff about your complaints procedure

Ensure your organisation has a well-publicised complaints procedure which actively asserts that it is open to receiving and listening to complaints from service users, their friends, families and other supporters.

Explain how it works

Actively inform the people you care for that they can make complaints, should they need to, and explain the process. Reassure them that they will be listened to, that complaints will not be shelved, and action will be taken to investigate the circumstances of the complaint fully.

Give assurance that complaints will be handled fairly and genuinely

Don't fob complainants off with empty words. Show respect for them at all times and deal with the matter in confidence. Details should not be discussed casually with members of staff or others unconnected with the complaint. Complaints are not matters to gossip about.

Investigate objectively

Evidence should be actively sought and assessed objectively by an individual with no direct involvement in the issues in dispute. If complaints are being made about individual members of staff, treat those individuals with respect and give them every opportunity to give their side of the story. The notion of 'due process' should apply all round, even where you decide you have to suspend a member of staff during the investigation of alleged serious wrongdoing.

Get on and deal with a complaint

Don't let complaints drag on. If they are not dealt with speedily and effectively, relationships may be poisoned, leading to deteriorating morale among service users and staff alike.

Understand what has happened and how it has happened

Perhaps a member of staff has acted inappropriately, or maybe organisational procedures are the cause – explore and understand how this has happened. If the complaints handler decides the complaint is unfounded, explore why the complainant felt the need to make it. Making complaints may be a sign of deeper worries. Try to rebuild poor relationships that may have developed. Ask the individual's key worker to pay special attention to anything that might be going wrong.

Accept responsibility whenever appropriate

If the provider (you, your staff or the 'system') is shown to be at fault, accept that you are in the wrong. Take action where necessary (disciplinary measures; care practice improvement; compensation if appropriate; referral to an outside body). Don't try to evade responsibility, but always be careful to ensure that rights under employment law are not overridden, especially in coming to a decision about dismissal where a complaint is upheld. Your complaints procedure must always be underpinned by the law.

"When complaints are freely heard, deeply considered, and speedily reformed, then is utmost bound of civil liberty attained that wise men look for."

– JOHN MILTON, FROM AREOPAGITICA (1644)

Feed outcomes back to staff

Provide specific feedback to the staff member(s) concerned. Provide general feedback, without breaching confidentiality, to staff as a whole. Supervision sessions with individuals and staff meetings are useful for giving feedback and discussing how improvements can be made.

Learn lessons from complaints

Keep detailed records of all complaints. Review them regularly to see if any patterns emerge. Are particular aspects of the service or particular staff groups or individuals complained about more often than others? Have patterns changed over time? Spot the weak points and change them. Handled well, complaints can become a powerful and effective management tool for quality improvement. Make use of them!

And lastly...

This open and fair approach should apply to staff too. In this way, line management and staff consultation processes will mean that complaints from staff are heard and acted upon – thus avoiding the need that some staff might otherwise feel to resort to whistleblowing.

Management dos and don'ts you can't afford to ignore

Victoria Metcalfe *has worked for more than 25 years in various positions with and for people living with dementia, including social services, the Alzheimer's Society and Anchor.*

There is no blueprint to be a good care home manager but there are some personal attributes that tend to be common in a great care home manager. They have aspirational vision, huge reserves of positive energy, are motivational, creative and are as flexible as a rubber toy. There are heaps of books about management but you won't go far wrong by simply applying person-centred principles to every aspect of your role and never forget 'people can't give what they don't get'.

There is a lack of communication in here!

Role model good communication skills with your team to create a culture of positive communication where people don't just listen to each other – they hear what is being communicated. Praise and encourage those who do, and for those who don't, support them to develop their skills.

Principles and vision

Remember: talking about principles and painting your vision is not enough – it fades. Spend time with your team, illustrate the picture with real examples and keep it alive. Involve everyone and explain why they and their talents are essential to fulfil the vision.

Communicate your passion

Be a role model in every action you take and every decision you make. Positive energy creates positive energy. Be creative without fear – being risk adverse limits creativity. Be open, honest and create an environment where being spontaneous and courageous are positive personal attributes.

Treat quality systems as your slave and not your master

Remember they are there to help you and keep everyone safe. Send that message, provide opportunities for individual development to use and apply these systems and your team will view them as tools of the trade to help, guide and support.

Inspire everyone to be a leader

Invest in your natural leaders. Challenge your team to find the answers. Stimulate innovation and empower the team to find better ways to do things. Have the humanity to grasp the fact that you don't always have all the answers. Don't over-analyse other people's ideas, there may be some failures along the way but there will be successes – celebrate them.

Value-based recruitment

Look for people who are far more than naturally empathetic and kind – that must be a basic requirement. You don't want a happy comfortable team, you need passionate energetic people who are ready to take on a challenge. Always include your customers in the recruitment process – they will bring a wealth of wisdom and experience.

Lead by example and walk the talk

Use every opportunity to develop your team, individually and in groups. In the same way we validate a customer's feelings consider this approach with your team. Provide opportunities to debrief individuals – they will need this time with you to grow.

Connections and relationships are your business

Remember that valuing the worth of each individual goes beyond the customer group; it applies to everyone in the location and those who visit. Recognise the uniqueness of each person and be aware of the emotional state of individuals. Be open, honest and create an environment of trust – this is the key to balanced relationships.

"Be the change you want to see in the world."

– Mahatma Ghandi

"If you keep doing what you always do, you will keep getting what you always got."

– Anon.

Supervision and individual support

Invest in your team by ensuring they know they are valued. Use supervision time to praise what has gone well and develop positive steps to improve any areas of personal development.

What about you?

Don't neglect your own support and development. Your wellbeing is as important as everyone else's. Find someone who is authentic and inspires and challenges you – you need nurturing too.

Nursing for non-nursing managers: issues which may prove challenging

TRACY PAINE

is operations director for Belong, member of the RCN Older People's Forum and chairs the NCF Practice Forum. Healthcare Design Champion, 2011.

There is a recognised shortage of registered nurses, and few make a positive choice to work in care homes. Innovative providers have risen to this challenge and reviewed the role of the nurse within the wider team by developing alternative models of care that are more attractive to the modern workforce and will meet the complex needs of today's customer. The art of people management is a vocation in itself; therefore a good manager is more than capable of getting the best possible care for their customers without being a nurse, but recognises a nurse's value.

You need nurses

Embrace nurses as a vital part of your team; not a bolt-on extra. Nurses are compassionate and have committed themselves to providing care to others at a time of need, so take full advantage of their skills, experience and clinical judgement.

Your customers need nurses

Healthcare is paramount. Nurses use their clinical judgement to help improve, maintain or recover good health. Nurses can instil confidence with customers, families and professionals. During periods of ill health or at the end of life, you will need their specialist knowledge and skills.

Nurses need you

Nurses need to feel valued and acknowledged as important members of the team. Make sure they are included in your organisation's plan, with clear objectives and regular support. Identify a lead for your team to provide clinical support, direction and act as a conduit between nurses, managers and staff.

Work in partnership

Create an environment that fosters good relationships with community and specialist nurses. Nurses are independent practitioners who should be supported and encouraged to work with healthcare colleagues to define a plan of care that avoids bureaucracy and focuses on the best outcome for the customer.

Dispel the myths

Spending hours giving out medicines is not considered to be the best use of nurses' time, so release them from the shackles of the medication trolley. Use the NMC (Nursing and Midwifery Council) guidance around safe delegation, accountability and decision-making. Nurses have much more to offer to your customers.

Recruit to shared values

Don't be tempted to recruit a nurse for their qualification alone. Nurses are key to your business and they should be aligned with your organisation's values. Promoting your values as part of your advertising and selection process will help attract candidates and stand you out from the competition.

Be courageous

Challenge nurses, regulators and other healthcare professionals who may have their own ideas of what nurses working in care homes should or should not be doing. Always put the customer at the centre of all that you do and in all decisions to be made.

"I've learned that people will forget what you said, people will forget what you did, but people will never forget how you made them feel."

– MAYA ANGELOU

Invest in your teams

Nurses are accountable for their decisions to delegate to colleagues. Investment in training and developing your workforce will ensure your staff have the necessary skills and knowledge to meet the needs of the customer and will help retain good people.

Recognise achievements

Nominate nurses for awards. It's a great way to share best practice and national coverage promotes a sense of achievement for all.

Make every contact count

A nurse's time is valuable so share it wisely among your customers. Make sure nurses focus on the things non-nurses can't do. Encourage them to plan their time well, delegate safely and record every contact with a customer. Nurses should contribute to and enhance the care plan using finely tuned assessment skills.

Understanding and working with the NHS – every challenge is an opportunity!

IRENE GRAY

has more than 41 years experience as a trained nurse including 28 years as an executive director in the NHS and more recently in the care home sector. She specialised in elderly care in the mid-1970s and has carried this experience with her throughout her career. Irene now works independently as a consultant, supporting the delivery of excellence in health and care leadership.

The health and social care sectors have never experienced as much challenge as they do today. The economic, demographic and epidemiological challenges provide a moving feast and will be driven by politics and political time frames. While the current climate may be seen as intimidating, both for delivery of excellent care and for business survival, there is almost certainly a significant opportunity to be harnessed. The need to think out of the box, to be savvy in our approach, to recognise the value we can add and be brave in making things happen, is undoubtedly the challenge. The systems need each other and moreover, the patient/service user, needs the sectors to be harmonised.

Deep suspicion

Accept from the start that there is in NHS staff a deep, ingrained suspicion of the independent sector which you must understand and acknowledge. There is nothing to be gained by refusing to accept the justification in part for this view because in the past there have been occasions when the performance of the independent sector has been less than ideal – remember Winterbourne View. That said, of course the failings of the Mid-Staffordshire NHS Foundation Trust as exposed in the Francis Report have highlighted that the NHS can be equally guilty.

Build relationships

These long held beliefs and lack of harmonised relationships between the NHS and the care home sector can be addressed through being brave and taking the initiative to build relationships.

Openness and transparency

Aim to build open and transparent credibility with the local acute Trust. Don't be inhibited by local commissioners. Do the key staff in the Trust really know who you are and what your home provides?

Be patient and persistent

Arrange to meet with the director of nursing and or key senior nursing staff in the Trust. Introduce yourself and be clear that you are concerned to build a firm relationship to ensure both services and the patient and residents can benefit. You may encounter initial resistance, missed or cancelled meetings, even hostility but be patient and very persistent.

Train with the Trust

Identify the challenges you face in your home and consider whether working with the NHS could help solve them. Lack of training and skills could be solved by accessing training at the Trust for your staff. It should be available at a reasonable rate, and your staff and the Trust staff will benefit from the relationship building.

Potential recruitment benefits
This relationship building could help your staffing issues. Should staff in the local hospitals think they might like a move, they could be persuaded – for the first time ever in many cases – to work with you.

Share experiences
Remember that most NHS staff will never have worked in a care home or even understand the independent model. Likewise, many of your staff will never have worked in an NHS trust. Look for and arrange shared experiences. Try to arrange for your staff to work in local hospitals and for their staff to work in your care home. Understanding and relationships built this way are invaluable.

Case Study
A busy acute NHS Trust is surrounded by care homes. Trust staff feel frustrated because the homes seem to be slow accepting their residents back. A senior Trust nurse decides to create a link with some of the local homes to share learning on managing dementia and pressure ulcers. The link changes attitudes, achieving shared respect and improved care for residents. There is still a long way to go! This is the tip of the iceberg.

Provide solutions
Try to provide solutions for your local acute Trust's major challenge which is how to move patients from its expensive beds to suitable new environments. These could vary from providing intermediate care, to convalescence, even day care (if this provides a reassuring presence which will speed discharge home).

Seeing it with their eyes
Can some of your staff spend a day in the local Emergency Department to observe how it works and what the challenges are? Can they shadow the discharge co-ordinator to understand the challenges they face in discharging patients. It could help to meet some of the social workers who are so often expected to provide discharge solutions at short notice.

Invite staff to visit
Host a day for key staff from the acute Trust to learn about your home, how it functions and how it is regulated. Remember that regulatory standards are quite different, even though you have the same regulator. Learn from attendees of the challenges they have and look for opportunities of breaking down barriers and sharing expertise.

Being creative is central to you delivering quality care

CHRIS GAGE

is director of Ladder to the Moon which delivers training and creative engagements for older people and their supporters that result in improved quality of life and business outcomes.

At a time when there's great need for new solutions and ways of doing things in the care sector, one of the big challenges, as I see it, is to enable people throughout care organisations to bring their creativity to bear. If creative behaviors are regularly expressed in care communities, then those services will be supporting great outcomes for people; they'll provide enjoyable environments to live and work in, and passionate people will want to be working there. For this to happen, the sector needs leaders who actively embody creative behaviours and support their staff to do the same.

We are all creative

Have you ever heard it said: "I'm not creative!" This common idea is a myth; we're all creative. We all use creativity to problem-solve in our lives and come up with new solutions; whether replacing an ingredient when cooking, thinking of a present for a friend or finding ways to rearrange our busy schedules.

We need to redefine creativity

While the artistic expressions of creativity, such as painting or performing, have enormous value, this kind of creativity is not the most crucial to our day-to-day wellbeing or that of the people we support. We're really talking about creativity as a mindset: being open, flexible, having fun, finding connections and embracing possibility.

Creativity is at the heart of healthy businesses

The importance of creativity was reflected in results of an IBM survey. Fifteen hundred chief executives from 33 industries worldwide concluded that more than rigour, management discipline, integrity or even vision, successfully navigating an increasing complex world will require creativity.

Creativity causes quality care

Organisations which want their services to deliver great outcomes, with a stable and productive staff team showing spontaneity and flexibility, need to say they want people to have fun and be creative.

Leadership for creativity is crucial

Leadership is essential to making creative care cultures a reality. People need to feel enabled to express themselves and to come up with new ways of doing things. Permission needs to be granted at all sorts of levels, from managing director to cleaner.

The need to follow-through
This intention needs to be backed up with the way training is delivered, with all policies, and with recruitment.

Step back and lose out
We sometimes meet managers who see it as someone else's role to have fun, take a risk, share something of themselves or step outside their comfort zone. They stand at the edge and watch, or push people on a course without engaging with change themselves. They have little lasting impact in these settings.

Take part and see results
We also meet managers and team leaders who are willing to foster creative attitudes in themselves and their staff. These are managers who achieve tangible benefits for their service as a result.

"I have become free enough back at work to allow my fun side out more. As managers, we can get too bogged down with always being the 'professional', but now I have allowed myself and my staff team to be more playful."

– DONNA STALLIBRASS, REGISTERED MANAGER AND LADDER TO THE MOON WORKSHOP PARTICIPANT

Each member of the team needs you
Even with great leadership, without a positive team response to new ideas it takes a big personality to put your head above the parapet. Conversely, a critical mass of creative people makes creativity 'catch on'. By focusing on encouraging creativity in each individual, we develop attitudes of being open, expressive and positive in the whole team.

This is fun
If you want the people around you to be adaptable, supportive and open; then you need to be the change that you want to see around you. Have fun, laugh, smile, nurture ideas, listen, say yes, embrace failure as learning, make positive comments when you see what you want to see, think big and most of all- enjoy yourself!

A positive future for care homes

PROF. JULIENNE MEYER

is Professor of Nursing at City University London, co-director of My Home Life programme, co-convenor of the National Care Homes Research & Development Forum.

TOM OWEN

has worked with older people for 27 years as a campaigner, researcher and practitioner. Tom is the co-founder and the co-director of My Home Life programme.

Despite the national policy towards supporting older people to remain in their own homes, the good news for care homes is that demand for beds is likely to double over the next 30 or so years. The population going into care homes is likely to be different, with more self-funders and residents who require increasing levels of intensive health and social care support. The challenge for all of us working in the care home sector is to respond positively together to both the ever-changing health and social care policy contexts and the changing needs, aspirations and circumstances of our older population.

A positive agenda

Simply knowing that care homes can play a positive role in supporting older people is not enough: we need to become a more active player, working in partnership with the public, with health and social care systems and with older people in helping to respond and shape a positive agenda for older people's care in the future.

Negative perceptions

The conditions for positive partnerships with the public and with external agencies need to be changed. At the moment the public have a deeply uncomfortable relationship with care homes, what they do and how they are funded. They are anxious about what they read in the press, they are uneasy with what care homes seem to represent: death, despair, frailty, vulnerability. This negativity and mistrust is also reflected in the attitudes, policies and behaviours of external agencies.

Homes must lead the change

To break this vicious cycle, *My Home Life* would argue that real sustainable change must begin within the sector. Homes can come across as defensive, lacking in confidence, 'closed' and disengaged and this serves only to confirm outside suspicions that they cannot be trusted. Care homes must stop operating from a position of threat and fear of things going wrong.

Engage with confidence and openness

The sector needs to behave in ways that challenge what we think of care homes. It needs to communicate with confidence and with a spirit of openness, embracing opportunities to act in partnership with older people, their families, external professionals and the public.

A single voice

The sector needs to convey to the world its expertise, communicating as a single voice what it is seeking to do in responding to the aspirations of older people and the challenges facing the health and social care system.

An evidence base

Historically, it has been others (regulators and commissioners) who have defined what care homes should be doing. Instead the sector needs to 'own' the agenda by developing its own evidence base for quality.

Self-confidence and professionalism

From this basis, the care home sector should be articulating how it will improve, the support it needs and the support it can offer others in taking forward our collective agenda for improving the lives of frail older people. By these means care homes will rightly start to communicate a sense of self-confidence and professionalism which will help to challenge the deep-rooted negative thoughts about the sector.

Focus on leadership

My Home Life would argue that it is the care home manager that is pivotal to changing the sector's relationship with the wider world. *My Home Life* has already identified that by supporting the leadership and professional expertise of managers, by offering them time and space to work together to develop their resilience and share their expertise, they are better placed to take forward the quality agenda in partnership with the public, with families and with external professionals.

"Be in no doubt, a small group of thoughtful, committed people could change the world. Indeed it's the only things that ever has."

– MARGARET MEAD

A better understanding

By working towards and articulating a shared evidence-based, relationship-centred vision for care homes (see www.myhomelife.org.uk for more information), the sector can help the public and the wider health and social care system understand better the professional role they can play and how this fits within the broader aspirations for care of older people.

A tipping point for change

As a movement of care home practitioners, *My Home Life* is trying to take forward this agenda. We hope that as more care home practitioners come together with one vision, so we will witness a tipping point, where suddenly a different type of voice emerges from the care home sector – a voice which communicates confidence, pride and expertise. This will ultimately serve to challenge the world's fears about care homes and help the sector move forwards positively into the future.

4

Promoting your home successfully

The foundations of marketing

I passionately believe that marketing and communications, when used effectively, can play a vital role in supporting care services – helping them to reach new customers, develop reputation and celebrate their tremendous work. In this chapter, I've tried to explain some of the foundations that you need to consider before investing in any marketing activity. By understanding these key principles, you'll be able to get things right: engaging the right people, using the right methods and saying the right things.

JOHN HUGHES

is a communications & marketing manager for Community Integrated Care, one of the UK's largest social care charities, and a Chartered Marketer.

The starting-point

What is 'marketing'? It's certainly not just leaflets, adverts and newspaper coverage. Perhaps the simplest definition is that marketing is a process of understanding and meeting your customer's needs, expectations and desires, to support your business' aims. So, before producing glossy adverts, let's take a step back and consider what marketing means in your service . . .

Brilliant brands

Every good brand, from a popular supermarket to a care home with a long waiting-list, shares common positive qualities. They focus on customers, stand-out from competition, are dependable, solve their customer's problems and are easy to access. To be truly marketable, your home needs to have these same qualities.

You can do it!

Resources in the care sector can be restrictive, but this needn't stop your service having the attributes of a successful brand. I've seen amazing examples of services acting ambitiously, without creating any extra expense.

Think creatively

An example: One of our services formed a partnership with occupational therapy students from their local university to develop specialist tools to enhance the life-skills of the people they support. This was a great example of being customer-focused, solving problems and standing out from the crowd, without spending more money. This made an amazing statement and frankly, was easy to promote.

Have a plan

So, your service now has the qualities of a great brand - time to get promoting it then, right? Well, first you need to know who you are marketing to and why. Too often, care services waste money marketing themselves, guided only by 'gut instincts'.

Know your audiences

A good marketing plan for a care home focuses on the people or groups who interact with or can influence it. Consider what your audiences expect of you, what they can offer to your home, and how you can deliver a better service to them. This understanding will guide your choice of marketing activities.

Relationships are key

Building a relationship with customers is the ultimate goal of marketing. Sure, leaflets and adverts can be great, but they rarely match a great interaction with another person. If you know your audiences well, you'll know what will engage them and spark a great relationship.

An example

You need to improve occupancy in your home and can spend £1,000 on a local newspaper advert, which is read by thousands of people – sounds good? Well, the newspaper might be read by many people, but how many of its readers are looking for care? Likely a small fraction – suddenly the advert looks less cost-effective. Perhaps there are other ways to gain referrals, like building great relationships with local social workers and carer's forums.

"Your work is going to fill a large part of your life, and the only way to be truly satisfied is to do what you believe is great work. And the only way to do great work is to love what you do."

– Steve Jobs

Use your ambassadors

Care homes are filled with passionate, dedicated people: staff, families and the people they support. They are your greatest promotional asset, because it is their contribution which makes your service special. Whatever promotional tools you choose to use, involve your home community wherever possible.

Become a marketeer!

Marketing is common-sense, but it does require skills and experience, so strive to develop yours. If you work for a large organisation, learn from your marketing department or, if you work for a smaller care provider without a marketing resource, perhaps see if local marketing students can volunteer to assist you. There is always something new to learn!

Placing your home at the heart of the community : Practical ideas

The quality of life of older people in care homes is not just the responsibility of the proprietor, manager and staff in the home – it has to be the responsibility of all of us in society. We all need to feel a connection with the wider world; the places, people and things that contribute to who we are, and provide us with a sense of security, belonging, continuity, purpose, achievement, and significance. Sadly, care homes often feel isolated from or forgotten by the local community. Fortunately, many care homes across the country are now going the extra mile to connect purposefully with their local communities. Some ideas from *My Home Life*:

Tom Owen

has worked with older people for 27 years as a campaigner, researcher and practitioner. Tom is the co-founder and the co-director of My Home Life, a UK programme (and social movement) promoting quality of life for those living, dying, visiting and working in care homes.

The needs of your residents and staff

Work with your staff, relatives and residents to think creatively about how community involvement might help respond to the wide range of needs of residents. Consider how you can connect them with places they used to frequent and the friends and interests that they previously had.

The needs of the community

Think about what would motivate members of the community to engage with the home. What information, education and support do they need to help them feel comfortable in being with people who may have significant mental and physical health problems? Putting on talks for community organisations or a stall in the local market can help outsiders understand what you are trying to do in the home.

Putting on events in the home

Remember that times of day might suit different people in terms of visiting the home or joining your parties. Remember first impressions count – if visitors feel valued and listened to, they are more likely to return and tell others to join in too.

Recruiting volunteers

Rather than putting out a general call for volunteers, why not identify a specific need within the home and recruit individuals with the skills that can address this need?

Schools and colleges

Intergenerational work can be as positive for children as it is for residents. Schools and colleges might value engaging with you in helping deliver student projects or in meeting their curriculum on 'citizenship' agenda.

Churches

Write to your local churches or community groups to explore ways of working together. Perhaps you could offer them a free space in the home where they could meet (provided they welcome your residents, relatives and staff to join them).

Physical space

Ensure that communal areas, individual rooms and outside areas are arranged so that people have access to quiet spaces and private areas to talk to one another.

Technology

Offering residents, relatives and staff access to Skype and internet networks is also a great way to help connect care homes to other communities.

Recognise the value to your business

Community engagement can have a positive impact upon the culture of the home, helping staff to see things through 'fresh eyes' and feel more valued. It can help build the home's reputation and increase occupancy rates. Perhaps most importantly, in these days of funding cuts, the community can help raise funds or provide extra activities in the home.

Community starts 'within'

Managers need to recognise that community starts from within the home in helping staff, residents and relatives to connect emotionally; enabling them to recognise the reciprocal nature of care; and appreciate how every member of the 'care home community' can offer something to the whole. If the outside world experiences a real sense of warmth and engagement between staff, residents and relatives- they will be more attracted to being part of it.

(more ideas on the website: www.mythologies.org.uk)

Achieving great occupancy levels

EMMA CHARLTON

is the marketing director at Caring Homes. Working with home managers, Emma secures some of the highest occupancy levels in the sector.

It may sound like a truism, but delivering outstanding customer service lies at the very heart of achieving high occupancy levels. Every resident, or prospective resident, must be thought of as a valued customer – a customer who could very easily take their business elsewhere if they don't receive great customer service from you. It is essential that everyone working in a care home has a positive customer service attitude – from the home manager to care support workers, each member of the care team has a key role to play in delivering the very best service.

First impressions count

From the moment a prospective resident or family member picks up the phone or walks through the door, they should know their needs are your priority. You wouldn't stand for poor customer service and neither will they.

Creating a customer service culture

Instilling a positive customer service culture isn't easy, but it can be done. The benefits to your residents and your business are absolutely worth the effort. A great resource is Michael Heppell's '5 Star Service'. This offers excellent tools to help achieve your goals.

Know how and where to find your customers

Over half of your customers may come via a direct referrer. Whether this is a hospital discharge co-ordinator, social worker or fund holder, these professionals should know who you are, and what great customer service your home delivers.

Don't cast your net too wide

Eighty per cent of your potential customers live less than half an hour from your home. This is your target catchment area and should be the focus of your attention and marketing budget.

Reputation, reputation, reputation

Consistently excellent customer service will help to cement your reputation, the most important motivating factor in purchasing decisions. Build your reputation, promote it and protect it. Never take it for granted – it can take months and years to build, but can be lost overnight. Negative news stories remain online forever.

Building networks within your community

Your home is an important part of the local community. Make sure you build networks with local groups like Age UK and the Alzheimer's Society. Good relations with groups like this will contribute to your reputation-building. Don't forget to build networks with other good homes in your area – as much as 11% of your customers will come from other care homes.

Local advertising and press

Don't forget to advertise in local newspapers and magazines. When you are holding an event, such as a summer fair or Christmas party, invite your paper to send a photographer to record the event. Good news stories help build your reputation.

"Every resident or prospective resident should be treated as a valued customer. An excellent reputation and excellent customer service will deliver great occupancy levels."

Local opinion-formers

Thirty per cent of customers come from private households where your reputation will be key to their decision. Ensure you have a good relationship with the people who influence local opinion, such as local GP practices, councillors, churches, women's groups e.g. WI, U3A, Lions, Round Table and others.

Your contacts are the key to your success

When you meet someone always exchange contact details and keep a log of who you met. You can then use this contact network when you have vacancies. They may help by referring customers.

Understanding the sensitivity of the purchase

Very often, a care home admission will be driven by a 'health crisis'. This is a traumatic time for all concerned. You should make the process as simple, stress free and pleasant as possible. Excellent customer service will ensure your customers know your home is the right home.

Helping your staff to be your home's best salespeople

ALISON MESSENGER

is director of the Elder Homes Group – consisting of 14 care homes across the United Kingdom, specialising in various care bands from physically disabled, nursing, dementia, respite, mental health, residential and palliative care. Alison Messenger's ethos of "constantly caring" shines through in her outlook towards staff, residents and families.

In our opinion the term 'sales' tends to feel somewhat out of place, given the caring nature of our business. However, without some form of sales representation there would be no business existence. In practice we prefer to use the term 'customer service'. We feel that it is more appropriate for staff to be associated with this term of speech. The term "sales" can often scare and inhibit staff, subsequently having a negative impact on their psychological outlook, resulting in failure in the task before it is undertaken. This is the approach which we adopt here at Elder Homes.

Everyone is involved

Every member of our team – without exception – here at Elder Homes is considered to be a fundamental part of our sales, vision and strategy.

Get the service right first

We believe successful selling will be a natural result provided you are providing excellent care. You have to get this service right first.

Staff motivation

Encouraging, guiding, training, rewarding and awarding our staff is all part and parcel of our energy at Elder Homes. With consistency in all these factors comes the required positivity and trust for great selling and this, in turn, creates an abundance of positive outcomes.

Equip your staff

We find that giving our staff the tools needed to do the job delivers a genuine and transparent service. Subsequently staff will reassuringly and comfortably talk about themselves, our service and our care with confidence.

'Mystery shopping'

Our ethos within Elder Homes is simple: anyone who has eyes, ears and a mouth are potential sales staff. We have an outstandingly successful customer service department as well as a customer service training department which teaches all our staff good basic customer service skills, making them aware of the impact our words, behaviour and body language have on our day-to-day practice. To evaluate performance we mystery shop our homes regularly which gives us valuable feedback on all aspects of our homes. We use our findings to guide and enhance further training.

Specialist personnel

In addition to our training of all staff, a pool of designated staff are trained in-depth on advanced customer service skills, and are on hand in our homes to provide and deliver the service each of our potential customers deserves.

First impressions

First impressions count and, since we feel that every department plays a part in our customers' experience and outcome, we provide our staff from the home managers to maintenance staff with full and up-to-date audit tools to assist in making sure that customers' first experience is amazing and that these high standards are maintained, from the car park, front entrance, throughout the home down to our show room.

"People buy from people, as simple as that, and this comes from the heart. In our view this sums up our sector: It should all come from the heart."

Follow-up and involvement

We encourage and practice follow-up communication. We invite and welcome an additional comfort visit back to the home being considered by family members, friends or loved ones. This, we feel, enables any further questions to be answered and provides another chance to view the home, to speak with staff and take in, for a second time, an overall vital viewing. We believe that the more involvement our potential customers have with our team the more comfortable the experience will be and this is where the all important relationship begins.

Listen to potential customers

Potential customers have opinions and questions and it is vital that we are there to listen carefully and answer any questions which our customers may have to assist them in making that all-important decision of choosing the right care for their loved ones. Remember too that these customers may be able to provide valuable feedback which will help to make the next sales opportunity even more successful.

It comes from the heart

Having said all of this, we feel that all the above is just the icing on the cake. We can do our best to train staff to be impressive, knowledgeable, charismatic, engaging, interested, and reassuring. But people buy from people, as simple as that, and this comes from the heart. In our view this sums up our sector: it should all come from the heart.

Using electronic marketing successfully

DAVINA LUDLOW

has been a director of carehome.co.uk for more than 15 years. carehome.co.uk is the leading care home website in the care sector with more than 15 million visitors a year. Davina's aim is to promote good care and she is 100% dedicated to the care home sector.

On-line marketing or alternatively, internet marketing, is the dominant form of marketing currently used today. When looking for care for either themselves or a loved one, more than 70% of the population start searching via the internet to ascertain what type of care is available and where the most suitable care can be located. It is vital that a high percentage of your marketing budget is allocated to online activities.

Getting your message out

It is of prime importance that you get to that client ahead of anyone else with all of the information they will require to make a decision, and the quickest and easiest way is via the internet.

On-line options

There are many methods in which you can promote your care home via the internet including creating your own website, search engine marketing, using care home directory/review websites and through social media.

Templates: cheap but time-consuming

To create a website which is proficient to act as the platform for your marketing can cost thousands of pounds. However, there are templates available which can be used for you to create your own website and these are relatively cheap, but can prove to be very time consuming and labour intensive.

Ease of navigation

The most successful websites are those that contain all of the content required by the user and are simple to navigate.

Domain name – a crucial consideration

One of the most crucial decisions that must be taken into consideration when creating a website is that you choose the right domain name which is relevant to your care home and easily identifiable by the user.

Search engine optimisation

It is important that your website can be found on search engines. You should identify which key words people would use to search for a care home in your area (e.g. Care Homes Hungerford) and ensure these terms are used within your web pages.

Online directories

You can also drive traffic to your website by making sure that you have a presence on the key directory/reviews websites that specialise in care homes. Research the internet to ascertain which of these websites are the most popular and receive the most traffic. Assess which of the promotional options seem best value relative to the level of traffic. Most of these types of website offer enhanced listings or display advertising (banner adverts). As a general rule, it is best to focus your efforts on a couple of the key websites.

Enabling comparison

A further advantage to being on directory/review websites is that it will place your care home alongside competitors where you can then promote your services to their best advantages and explain why you believe your care home would be the best choice and provide the best care. Most websites of this nature allow you to post photographs, descriptions and reviews and it is imperative that you show your home to be the best choice for your customers.

"You can buy attention (advertising). You can beg for attention from the media (PR). You can bug people one at a time to get attention (sales). Or you can earn attention by creating something interesting and valuable and then publishing it online for free."

– David Meerman Scott

Using social media

Using social media is now an important way of promoting your care home on-line. Twitter, Facebook and Google+ are the most popular social media platforms, however Twitter is probably the one to focus on. It is a good idea to tweet upcoming events and any developments at the care home, ideally linking these tweets to additional information on your website.

Downloadable brochures

One of the many advantages to promoting your care home online is that the user has instant access to information and they can do their research in their own time and in their own space, however unsociable the hour may be. In these fast paced days the public now expect immediate access to information and it is helpful if they can download a pdf of the care home brochure which they can browse at their leisure. Of course it is always preferable to feel a nice glossy brochure in your hands, but this can follow later.

Using social media successfully

KEVIN CRAIG

is the managing director of Political Lobbying and Media Relations (PLMR). PLMR's award-winning team advise many of the UK's biggest care providers on PR, crisis management and social media.

F acebook, Twitter, Instagram. If those three words raise the hairs on the back of your neck, fear not. They're just another way of communicating with staff, residents, their families and the communities you serve, allowing you to show the excellent care you offer. Just like newsletters, noticeboards or a photo-wall inside a home. Except with one huge difference. Anyone can contribute or respond, praise or criticise, at any time. Unlike a newsletter, the control of what's written doesn't automatically default to you, the care home manager. That means there are risks, but also opportunities...

The Golden Rule: think before you post

If there's one thing to remember, it's this: everything you post on social media stays online. For ever. It's searchable and shareable, by anyone. For ever. Sobering, isn't it? So apply a 'sense check' before you post anything. Stop and think before you send.

Seek permission, not forgiveness

Of course, the above assumes you've cleared the use of social media with people at the highest level of your organisation. It's a conversation you need to have, before you start. Does your organisation have a social media policy? Do they have a Facebook page or Twitter account? Are they happy for you to set one up for your home?

Practice makes perfect

So you have permission, but you've never used social media before. Find someone who knows the basics, and ask them to help you practice in a safe environment, away from work. Learn how to create an account, how to post, how to 'like'. Understand the etiquette. Practice.

What should I post?

Stick to the facts, steer clear of opinion. "Residents of Example House really enjoyed today's visit from the owl man" tells you everything you need to know. Don't try to be funny. Simple is best. Include the name of your home, so people can find your message.

Respect the dignity of your residents

Your residents' care, privacy and dignity is your primary concern. If you're planning to post pictures of them, first make sure you have permission, from them or their families. It's worth the effort. A picture of happy, engaged residents enjoying an event at your home can send a powerful message of reassurance to their loved ones.

Give one person final responsibility

Our experience shows mistakes happen when there are too many cooks. One person posting on an 'official' account maintains consistency and control.

This is too much hassle. Why bother?

Because ultimately, social media allows communities of people (your stakeholders) with a shared interest (your residents) to stay in touch more easily. Isolation is one of the biggest problems facing elderly people. Think how reassuring it would be for the relatives of people in your care to get an update each day about the community their loved one is part of.

Help drive up occupancy

Which home would you choose for your loved ones? The one where it's difficult to find out what it's really like to live there, beyond the rhetoric of a brochure? Or the one which is open about the daily life of residents, highlighting the fantastic care they receive? Social media opens that window, allowing you to make your home as appealing as possible to current and potential residents and their families.

"Which home would you choose for your loved ones? The one where it's difficult to find out what it's really like to live there, beyond the rhetoric of a brochure? Or the one which is open about the daily life of residents, highlighting the fantastic care they receive? Social media opens that window."

Show your home in its best light

Keep it positive. It's your chance to tell everyone in your community of residents, relatives and carers about the great work you're doing. Report events, entertainment, and visitors. Post before an event, and share the experience afterwards. Use photos, if you have permission. Use SEO (Search Engine Optimisation).

Crisis? Help!

Angry messages? The wrong kind of Facebook or Twitter coverage? Media interest? Avoid getting into a public argument online. Call in some expert help – quickly.

Using the written word successfully

PAUL BRENNAN

Brennan has 35 years experience of marketing management. After working for many blue chip companies from diverse sectors, Paul has been in the healthcare sector for the past 13 years and is currently chief marketing officer for the Priory Group, which encompasses Priory healthcare and education, Craegmoor and Amore Care.

Every day most of us spend considerable time reading or writing. Nowadays it may have switched more towards PCs, ipads and the web rather than letters, printed adverts and books – but overall the changes in technology have simply increased the amount of reading and writing we do. Linked to this, all of us – indeed the entire population – are bombarded by more and more communication. The result is, whatever the nature of the written dialogue you are having, you must make sure it's clear, concise and effectively getting across your message, and therefore cuts through the clutter of the rest of the information overload all of us receive daily!

Adapt your style

With the proliferation of communication channels now available, one has to be more sure than ever about the appropriateness of dialogue and particularly language used - adapting it accordingly. The written word in a letter has to be treated slightly differently to the shorter forms of wording used, for example, in emails or texts – let alone the style one should adopt for adverts or websites.

Positive warmth

Just as people, in speech, can tend to be closed or open in their questions and general approach, so in written communications these same nuances can come through. Obviously the feel and tone of 'closed' communication can seem distant and uninterested and therefore lacking the positive warmth which seems so relevant and appropriate to our services.

Making impact

Specifics rather than generalisations have far more impact and weight. A key paragraph or two making some convoluted point can be so general it fails to communicate the salient point. Alternatively a specific fact, or a statistic, can be delivered in a more impactful way by making it the basis of the communication.

Beware of over-abbreviation

Everyone who works in the health and social care arena will agree that the sector speaks in shorthand. Any opportunity to abbreviate a service or approach to a random set of letters – all seem to adopt them. Remember, however, that this doesn't give clarity to those new to the sector, nor to the public.

Keep it simple

The old adage of "K.I.S.S." – keep it simple, stupid – is a good basic point to keep in mind for all communication. Everyone has busy lives; today everyone is bombarded by messages all the time and therefore being sure any communication is clear and to the point is vital.

A professional manner

Impressions of an organisation are built on how staff embody the brand during any dealings they have with stakeholders. In reality one vital aspect of this translates into the need for all staff to communicate in an appropriate manner to everyone – professional or public – who they deal with.

Know the target audience

The nature of our services usually means we have to communicate to various audiences which I simplistically categorise above as professionals or public. This divergence in the target audience is important to understand and so make sure that the written words used and messages communicated are right for each group.

Use the right channel

Taking the above point one step further, not only do the words need to be right, but the channels of communication need to be right too. This should affect your thinking about all manner of issues, such as, is an advert, website or PR item appropriate for this audience or is a professional directly-addressed letter better?

"In reality one vital aspect of this translates into the need for all staff to communicate in a professional and appropriate manner to everyone."

Write how you would speak

People who verbally can quite articulately and succinctly make a point or explain a benefit (for example the benefits of their service), when faced with written communication frequently adopt the style and tone of an eighteenth century lawyer! Don't lose the emotion and benefits based approach when using the written word – write how you would speak.

Call to action

So to the end of your written communication, and what is the conclusion or 'call to action'? Too often long written communication concludes with the reader thinking "so what do they want me to do now?" Ensure that, in conclusion and summary, you make it clear what actions or options the reader of your communication now has.

Working with all forms of the media

Geoff Hodgson

has worked as a reporter, sub-editor, features writer and editor of several regional and community newspapers. He has been editor of Caring Times since 1998.

Local and regional newspapers and radio stations, village newsletters and community websites are the most significant media with which a care home manager is likely to engage. The main thing is to be media-conscious – newspapers, radio and other media can't spread your message if don't tell them about it. Care homes are part of the community and editors are conscious of their duty to reflect this. Be persistent – not every item you send will be published or broadcast and you are competing for limited space and airtime. The more you submit, the more chance there is of something being used.

Do it in-house

Media organisations have limited resources and they will rarely be able to send a reporter or photographer to your events. So take your own photographs and send these, along with a press release, to their news editor. Don't give up if two or three reports you send in are not used – your persistence will almost certainly pay off. Invite the local media to all your events – a lot of the time they won't turn up but sometimes they will and this helps to build rapport. Be approachable. Get to know your local media people.

Make it somebody's job

Publicity can get forgotten. See if you can persuade one staff member to be responsible for publicity and see that everything gets done (photos taken, checking spelling of people's names, having the press release approved by head office prior to sending out, etc).

Who to send it to?

Send everything to the news editor – they will want to see your article first before passing it on to the most appropriate person. If it goes first to say, the features editor, they may not appreciate the potential news value and fail to pass it on, as that is not such a fundamental part of their role. Find out the news editor's name – the personal touch always helps.

Photographs – make them stunning

Submit just one or two of your best photos of a particular event. Avoid posed photos of large groups or of people holding trophies, certificates or outsized 'cheques'. Editors want to make their pages look interesting, so send interesting photos – close-ups of residents with their carers or family members have much more visual appeal than mayors or other 'celebrities'. Be sure to provide a photo caption, including the names and titles (Mrs, Miss, Ms etc) and job titles of the people shown in the photo.

Good photos don't just happen

Ensure photos are high-resolution, in-focus and well-lit. Editors will not consider a poor quality photograph. If you are lucky, one of your staff may be a keen amateur photographer – ask around. Send photos as email attachments in jpeg format.

Press releases – the Four 'Ws'

Press releases are not hard to put together – just make sure they address the 'Four Ws': WHAT the event was about; WHEN it was held (or is going to be held); WHERE it took place (or is going to take place) and WHO are the key people involved. Keep it brief but be sure to include a named contact person, with email address and telephone number, in case further information is sought. Send press releases as email attachments in Word format. Be sure they have been approved for release by the appropriate people before sending them out.

Hidden talents

Know your staff – perhaps one has a flair for writing publicity material. Be aware of your staff's interests and hobbies – these can be a great source of stories to enhance the profile of your care home in the local community. Consider the possible publicity value of everything that happens: perhaps your laundry person is retiring after 15 years, or your home was rated 'excellent' by the CQC at the last inspection.

Case History

Emma, a senior carer, does Ikebana – Japanese flower arranging – as a hobby. She took some flowers in to the home and showed the residents how it's done. The local paper ran a little story with a lovely photo a staff member had taken of Emma helping a resident to do an arrangement.

Features

Can you, or someone else in your care home or organisation, write interesting features? An editor might jump at the chance of running an interview with one of your residents, or perhaps 'a day in the life of a care home manager'.

Community interaction

If you take some residents shopping, or to the local pub, this has a good chance of being mentioned as it shows community interaction and is good for both your care home and the pub (or other community facility visited). Participate in community events such as 'open garden' days. Be a part of National Care Home Open Day – www.nationalcare-homeopenday.org.uk – and be sure to tell your local media about it.

Comment on issues affecting your residents

Consider putting out press releases commenting on issues affecting older people. Local media doesn't always know who to go to for informed comment and they may be keen to know your views. A 'Letter to the Editor' from the manager of the local care home will carry a lot weight on issues ranging from local speed limits to refuse collection times.

5
Legal quagmires and pitfalls

Firing a member of staff

Mike Carroll

is lead consultant for Collinson Grant's employment law helpline. He advises many care providers and writes regularly for Caring Times.

It's never pleasant but it has to be done. And you'll feel a lot better if you do it right. Misbehaviour by the staff puts residents at risk. As Winterbourne View showed, ill-disciplined employees can turn your good reputation into a toxic brand. 'Treat others as you would like to be treated yourself' is a good guide to staying on the right side of the law. Employment tribunals always ask: 'Did the employer form a genuine belief? Was that belief based on reasonable grounds? Was that belief formed following a reasonable investigation? Was the dismissal within the band of reasonable responses?'

Start at the beginning

You will have already issued employees with a contract of employment. You may also have a handbook and, hopefully, grievance and disciplinary procedures. In any event, make sure you observe the ACAS Code of Practice. Train the staff in what you expect of them, including standards of conduct.

Follow your rules

If you have the above documents, then follow them. Tribunals will pay close attention to this, so you must be able to show that the process has been followed and that other sensible measures have been taken. Documentary evidence, such as records of meetings signed by employees, is best.

Establish the facts of the case

In your investigation, follow the mantra of 'who, what, why, where, when and how'. Do not prejudge. Interview everyone who was involved or on duty at the time. Have the investigation done by a manager who has had no previous involvement in the matter.

Stick to the process

Send a copy of the investigation report, and all other documentation that the company will be relying on, to the accused employee before any disciplinary hearing. The invitation to the hearing should explain: the allegation; its apparent seriousness and potential consequences (gross misconduct that could result in dismissal, for example); and the employee's right to be accompanied

Give them a fair hearing

The hearing is usually conducted by someone who has previously played no direct part in the issue – not a judge, jury, and executioner. Allow enough time for the hearing and make sure the employee or their companion has an opportunity to ask questions. Always adjourn to consider your decision.

The punishment should fit the crime

A tribunal will consider 'if dismissal was within the band of reasonable responses'. That is, not whether you think it was fair or what they think, but whether a 'reasonable employer' would have dismissed the person in those circumstances. Even for gross misconduct, demotion and a final written warning may sometimes be appropriate.

They can always appeal

You must always give the employee an opportunity to appeal against the outcome of a disciplinary hearing. Normally, the person hearing the appeal should, again, be someone who has not been directly involved previously and, of course, who has the authority, if necessary, to overturn the decision of the disciplinary officer.

Note it down

Notes should be made at all stages of the process: investigation, disciplinary hearing and the appeal. Remember that these may be used as evidence in any tribunal. These are not 'minutes', however. If possible, get the employee to sign them to confirm that they are an accurate record.

"Well, yes, I've fired a lot of people. Generally I like other people to fire, because it's always a lousy task."

– DONALD TRUMP

Be consistent, Mr Precedent

Consider whether and how you have dealt with any similar issues in the past. To what extent did you then set a precedent for the future? Recognise that unjustifiable inconsistency between cases may risk claims for unfair dismissal or discrimination.

But still treat each case on its merits

Always be fair and dispassionate and put your feelings towards the employee to one side. After all, that's how you would want to be treated if the boot was on the other foot. All situations are different, and consistency of standards and process doesn't always mean identical outcomes.

Mental capacity and Do Not Attempt to Resuscitate decisions – some legal issues

NEIL GRANT

is a partner at Ridouts solicitors. With more than 20 years' experience, Neil has a national reputation in defending the interests of care providers.

It is essential that managers and senior staff act lawfully when making end of life decisions in relation to service users who lack capacity. The requirements under the Mental Capacity Act 2005 are often misunderstood or ignored. One issue in particular has been the focus of frequent attention: the use of "Do Not Attempt to Resuscitate or "DNAR Orders" in care homes.

The effect of a DNAR Order

If a valid DNAR Order is in place it needs to be respected but only in relation to cardio-pulmonary resuscitation (CPR) and not to any other form of emergency care intervention.

What if there is no DNAR Order in place?

If there is no DNAR Order in place the expectation is that CPR will be undertaken.

Who should make the decision to put in place a DNAR Order?

As it is a clinical decision, the ultimate decision should be made by a doctor. In a care home context it will normally be the service user's GP, although a DNAR Order may originate from a hospital admission. Typically it will follow a multi-disciplinary team meeting. DNAR Orders should apply across care settings. The key factor is effective communication on transfer between services.

When should CPR be discussed with a service user, a representative or their family?

You will only need to discuss CPR with a service user, a representative or their family if a cardiac or respiratory arrest is a clear possibility. If the service user does not have capacity, you should inform any welfare attorney or court-appointed deputy of a decision not to attempt CPR, as well as family members.

What if there is a realistic chance that CPR could be successful?

If the service user has capacity, they can refuse CPR even if it would have a realistic chance of success. Similarly, a service user with capacity can set up an advance decision refusing CPR. If valid and applicable, the advance decision would need to be followed in the event of the service user no longer having capacity. However, if there is no advance decision in place and the service user lacks capacity, a best interests' decision should be taken.

Best interests' decision-making in relation to CPR

For incapacitated adults, the decision-maker should follow the statutory checklist under section 4 of the Mental Capacity Act 2005. This exercise should weigh-up the potential risks and burdens of CPR compared to the likely benefits. Consultation with a range of interested parties is required, including any welfare attorney or court-appointed deputy, as well as others close to the service user. If the potential risks and burdens of CPR are considered greater than the benefits, a DNAR Order should be put in place.

What if there are no family members?

If the service user is incapacitated, consideration should be given to appointing an Independent Mental Capacity Advocate (IMCA).

Coping with an emergency when there is no DNAR in place

While nurses in care homes with nursing should have the skills and experience to undertake CPR, carers in care homes without nursing may not. In residential care homes, what is important is that there are effective arrangements in place to summon emergency assistance from the ambulance service should the need arise.

"Managers and carers should reflect on their practice in relation to DNAR decision-making, given its importance in end of life care. Any DNAR decision must be made on the basis of an individual assessment of each service user, having proper regard to the requirements of the Mental Capacity Act."

What are the risks if proper decision-making is not in place?

There is a real risk of civil or criminal liability on the part of managers and carers. Complying with the Mental Capacity Act gives managers and carers a level of protection when making decisions in relation to adults without capacity. The Care Quality Commission is also focusing attention on Mental Capacity Act compliance and has taken enforcement action against managers, as well as providers, in relation to inadequate DNAR policies and practices.

Any other advice?

End of life decisions should be properly documented and reviewed regularly, including when circumstances change. It is a complex area of the law and advice should be sought if there is any uncertainty.

Warning notices – a word of warning!

JEREMY ALLIN

is a partner at Lester Aldridge LLP, and is a senior litigator and advocate of wide experience, now specialising in the care sector.

Amongst the armoury of weapons available to the Care Quality Commission (CQC) to ensure compliance by care providers with the requirements of the essential standards are Warning Notices. CQC can issue a Warning Notice to any provider who is in breach of one or more of the standards. Quite apart from concentrating the mind of the provider to a particular area, Warning Notices have many consequential effects some of which may be intended and some not.

Prevention is better than cure

A Warning Notice will only be issued following a finding of non-compliance at an inspection. It is essential to obtain feedback following inspection because CQC will not always say that they are going to issue a Warning Notice.

Take immediate action

If you receive a Warning Notice, look critically at the issue that has been raised. If there is a scintilla of truth to the alleged breach, take urgent action to correct it, whether that be by the simple expedient of doing something now, e.g. putting soap dispensers in bathrooms, or putting in place an action plan for issues that take longer to resolve, such as training provision or person-centred care planning.

Factual inaccuracies

After considering the notice, you must decide whether it is appropriate to make representations about any factual inaccuracies that are contained in the Warning Notice.

Refer to guidance

Make yourself familiar with the guidance issued to registered providers about Warning Notices. This sets out the procedure that CQC will follow if proposing to issue a Warning Notice.

Be aware of time limits

If you intend to make representations be aware that currently these must be made within 10 working days of receiving the notice. A Warning Notice is deemed to have been served the day after it was sent if it was sent electronically by email or on the third day after it was sent if served by registered post. If given in person it is the day on which it is delivered.

Remedy the breach

If representations are not appropriate, remedy the breach and take note of the time within which the breach is required to be remedied because you will be inspected on that day or very soon thereafter.

Serious consequences

Do not underestimate the importance of compliance with a Warning Notice. Failure to comply may result in a fixed penalty of up to £4,000 for each failure or the potential for further enforcement steps to be taken, either leading towards a proposal to cancel or vary the terms of the registration or to proceed down the criminal route.

Dealing with the press

CQC will issue a press release about the Warning Notice. This will be circulated to your local press. You must consider the impact that publication of the press release may have upon your service users and their relatives. You should consider calling a relatives meeting as soon as possible so that you can explain what has happened and what you have done about it. The support of relatives and service users is invaluable should you have to deal with the press.

"The greatest cultural achievement of a society is a contented older generation."

– JAPANESE PROVERB

Potential harm to residents

It is possible to persuade CQC that issuing a press release will cause more harm to service users than the harm that it is designed to cure, so consider that as an option and have very clear arguments as to how a press release will have a detrimental effect upon the service users rather than just your business.

A sensible approach

As a very general rule care providers' energies are better used in curing the breaches and managing the consequences of a Warning Notice than arguing about the content and then generally losing the argument!

Safeguarding investigations: how to minimise the risk of reputational damage

JONNY LANDAU

is a partner at Ridouts LLP and specialises in all areas of health and social care law with a particular emphasis on regulation.

The intention behind a co-ordinated, multi-agency approach to protecting vulnerable adults is undoubtedly laudable. After all, the true measure of any society can be found in how it treats its most vulnerable members. Safeguarding (or adult protection) investigations can, however, pose a considerable reputational risk to providers. All too often, external stakeholders take a prejudicial view of providers and are quick to share their judgments before providers are given a chance to respond. Once damaged, reputations can take an age to repair so it is vital to take control from the outset.

Take the initiative with stakeholders

Details of safeguarding referrals will be shared across a range of agencies. Commissioners, families and residents will have greater confidence in you if they hear from you before they hear from safeguarding and regulators.

Take professional PR advice

PR agencies can be an invaluable support when there is press or broadcast interest, or when serious allegations threaten important relationships. It is important that your voice is heard above the melee.

Understand the process

Read the local safeguarding policies in detail. Knowing the framework will help you take control when investigations snowball out of control. The local procedures may, for example, suggest timescales for the investigation that you can hold the Chair to.

Keep morale up

Staff can turn from being your most valuable asset to a real threat if they feel unsupported. Once morale is lost, staff often leave, whistle-blow and side with residents' families. Ask staff how you can help, listen carefully to their suggestions and make them feel valued.

Carry out your own investigation

Unless the police are involved and ask you not to, you have a duty to investigate any allegations. Determine for yourself whether the allegations are supported and be prepared to challenge other agencies when their findings are wrong.

Learn the lessons

What is done is done and cannot be undone. But recurrence of similar problems will pose a serious risk. Ask yourself whether you have real confidence in your quality assurance systems and seek external advice if needed.

Choose your battles

Stakeholders' concerns will be intensified if you do not acknowledge problems that are clearly evidenced. Build confidence by responding quickly and positively to allegations that are well-founded.

Put your best foot forward

If there has been a problem with your service, take particular effort to demonstrate how well you are doing in other areas. Try to ensure that you are judged by your usual good care rather than by an occasional lapse.

Keep your eye on other services

When one of your services is in crisis, it is easy for it to absorb all your time. Don't neglect your other services as slips elsewhere will raise concerns about systemic under-performance.

Be active as well as reactive

Formulate a plan taking into account the points above. Adapt it if necessary but have a clear strategy in mind from the start.

"Our reputation is more important than the last hundred million dollars."

– *Rupert Murdoch*

Legal dos and don'ts for care managers

KEITH M LEWIN

is senior partner of boutique law firm Brunswicks LLP, specialising in advising and representing care providers and their senior staff; author, editor, conference speaker.

Having represented care providers for many years there are some common themes which have emerged, this chapter represents a distillation of those themes and experiences. Many of the authors in this book are well known to me and their individual and collective experiences are well worth listening to; I don't always agree with them, nor do I necessarily share their individual opinions – but that is the delight of the professionals, there is often room for more than one opinion and more than one way to achieve a solution. So, to my top tips; much may seem trite, however, it is amazing how rarely they are followed:

Read, and inwardly digest, the contributions of my co-authors

The combined experience of the contributors to this book must exceed 1,000 years. Their comments and views as expressed in this book are a distillation of that experience and are worthy of close study. However, when reading, mentally challenge the views espoused, and seek to apply the more meaningful to your own circumstances.

Owners/regional managers should 'sign in'

Many are the times I have been instructed that the most senior people in a care organisation regularly visit a particular care home. However, when involved in a dispute with, say, CQC or the council one can be hard-pushed to prove the visits. A simple way is routinely to sign the 'Visitors' book.

If it is not written, it didn't happen!

Try to develop the habit of routinely making notes, not just 'to do' lists, but noting the contents of telephone conversations, meetings and so forth. If you are later challenged about an issue you will have a source of material which should confirm the situation.

Start using a 'Day Book'

To record your daily notes, don't use scraps of paper or the back of an envelope, use a bound book from which pages can't be readily detached, routinely date and sign the entries – all useful evidentially. It will help advisors formulate advice, and decide who is right!

Who are you dealing with?

It is often important to know who you met with, who you were speaking with during a telephone conversation and so on. So, routinely ask the person's name and, if appropriate, their status. Write it in your Day Book while noting the conversation.

If you are writing a record of an event, sign and date it

I regularly have seen crucial documents, including statements taken immediately after a key event, which are unsigned and undated . . .this undermines their usefulness. Make a habit of signing and dating all documents, and get your staff to do the same.

Meetings #1

I urge everyone when being summoned to a meeting to request in advance: an agenda, a list of who has been invited to the meeting, and their job titles. This information is vital to the preparation you undertake. If you intend having your lawyer alongside you, make sure that the person hosting the meeting knows this – your lawyer should attend to this.

Meetings #2

I encourage those attending meetings to have defined roles and for you to have your own minute-taker (in addition to any other minute-taker who might be present) – one can rarely concentrate on what a person is saying and formulate one's response while also making copious, coherent notes.

"I have seen two versions of the purported signed agreement. One of them does not have any form of signature next to the name... and bears no thumb-print. The other version of the document I have seen does have a signature... as well as a thumb print purportedly of the mother."

– MR JUSTICE WOOD IN DB v ZA, RA, THE METROPOLITAN POLICE AND LONDON BOROUGH OF CROYDON [2010]

Meetings #3

If tasks are assigned to you at a meeting, follow up with a letter or email to the person chairing the meeting to confirm your understanding of what you have been detailed to do, in what time-frame and with what output. Give a short but reasonable time for a response, say seven days.

Seek positive comments/observations

Public officials have a habit of seeking out the less compliant aspects of your business; after any inspection ask for oral feedback on the day, have someone with you to take a full note. At the end, if your service has been criticised, ask "And what matters did you find 'right', praiseworthy, even?" Follow up with an email or letter.

Managing the inspection process

PAUL RIDOUT

is a practicing solicitor who has specialised in health and social care law for more than 40 years and is currently head of Ridouts LLP.

External managed regulation is the yardstick by which the public may feel confidence in any health and social care service. Without objective and informed inspection the whole system breaks down. Providers and the public must both have mutual confidence in the impartiality, accuracy and proportionality of the inspection process. It is essential that providers understand their rights and obligations on inspection so as to be in a position both to contribute and, if necessary, to challenge.

Guidance for inspection management:

Always expect an inspection.

Do regular internal shadow inspections.

Use external consultants or managers not engaged in the service.

Visit and inspect out of hours.

When Care Quality Commission inspectors arrive – always ask for identification for anyone you do not know. ID should include authority to inspect! You are entitled to exclude anyone not authorised – consider if you wish to do that!

Make sure inspectors sign the visitors book.

Inspectors should be supported by your staff – constructive support is not obstruction.

Ask for regular feedback and note what the inspectors view, what they say and to whom they speak.

Staff may be interviewed privately but staff have the right to refuse. Staff should never be taken away from work. If such an interview is required it should be arranged when staff are off duty.

Service users may be interviewed in private but may refuse. They may need support. If the service user lacks capacity, the interview should not take place without a best interests decision. Service users will often require independent support.

Always insist on full feedback at the end of the inspection – no matter how late! Keep on asking "anything else" until the answer is no.

Make your own report of the inspection and possibly submit your report to the Care Quality Commission in advance of receiving their draft review.

If difficulties arise ask for copies of the inspector's contemporaneous notes.

"An appeaser is one who feeds a crocodile, hoping it will eat him last."
- *SIR WINSTON CHURCHILL*

6

Running a safe home

Balancing risk and benefits for residents

CAROLINE BAKER

is the head of quality & dementia care at Four Seasons Health Care. She has developed a tool to assess the impact of risk v benefit to help staff to make decisions about possible risk.

Coming into a care home should not prevent residents from enjoying the things they enjoyed at home. Preventing residents from carrying out the things that they want to do may create a greater risk of both physical frustration and psychological ill-being. What we need to do is weigh up the potential risk and impact of an activity against its likely benefit. We can then evaluate what may occur in terms of resistance, frustration, or becoming low in mood, if the resident is not allowed to take the proposed risk, and what benefits the resident might gain from allowing the activity to continue.

What is a risk?

A risk can be classified as anything that may potentially cause harm or danger. This may include a resident who likes to walk around the unit for most of the day but is at risk from falling as she or he is unsteady on their feet.

What is a benefit?

In terms of the resident experience in a care home a benefit can be described in terms of positive well-being. Interventions or 'allowing' interventions to take place that will help to raise self-esteem or help the resident to feel empowered and to maintain their independence, are benefits.

Assessing a risk

Staff will need to consider what the actual risk is, what the probability is of the risk occurring and what the impact and outcome might be if the risk occurred. For example, if the resident did fall and break his leg, in what ways might that affect him?

Assessing a benefit

Conversely, staff will need to consider the possible consequences if the risk were not allowed to be incurred, for example, if they constantly encouraged the resident to remain seated when he wanted to walk. The resident may become depressed, more dependent, more frustrated and hostile towards staff.

Life story

A knowledge of the resident's life story can have a huge bearing on how we take the risk-benefit decision forward. Did the resident enjoy activities that had a level of risk previously and what was their attitude to risk in general? How did the resident feel if they were not able to pursue an activity for any reason?

Including others

Speak to relatives and friends and establish how they feel about both the risk and the possible outcome. Ask them to consider how the resident might feel if they were prevented from carrying out their intended activity.

Best interest decisions

Bring all the relevant people together if the resident lacks capacity to make a decision and discuss the resident's wishes, the previous information that has been gained from life story work and the perspective of others that are involved.

Making the decision

Psychological harm can be as much of a risk as physical harm, if not more so. Staff, the relatives (and relevant professionals) need to agree a way forward that will determine which is the greater risk – completing the activity or not completing the activity?

"Life is inherently risky. There is only one big risk you should avoid at all costs, and that is the risk of doing nothing."

– Denis Waitley

Care plan

Staff need to document relevant conversations in detail and provide strategies for minimising the risk. For example, encouraging the resident to take regular rests at 'rest stops' along the corridor rather than asking them to remain seated in case they fall.

Impact & evaluation

How is the plan going? Is the resident at a level of well-being? Has the resident been exposed to any unknown or unplanned risks through carrying out the activity? If it was decided that the risk was higher than the benefit, how has this impacted on the resident's well-being or dependence?

Modern methods of monitoring your residents

MATTHEW TIMONEY

is a director of Medicare Systems Ltd. He is also a trustee for the musical charity Lost Chord which is committed to providing music therapy for people living with of dementia.

Today professional care is as much about recording data as it is about traditional concepts of caring for vulnerable people. The political, legal and media drive towards progressive accountability, has lead to supplementary benefits. One such benefit is that improved basic compliance auditing has become an effective management tool capable of protecting reputations, highlighting potential problems and even helping to fill bed spaces.

Monitoring: either end of the scale

Monitoring in UK care facilities ranges from care staff using tick sheets at one extreme right up to 24-hour tracking of both service users and carers at the other. The level of monitoring required is a management decision with wide ranging implications, however it is clear that the best care facilities can no longer afford to ignore automated monitoring data.

The benefit of automated evidence

Automatically recorded audit trails can furnish a clear insight into the quality of care being provided by any operator. Staff response times to nurse call activations, the length of time they spend with service users and the frequency of calls all provide valuable evidence as to the overall commitment to providing good service.

The basis of individual care

For long term service users, care plans provide the framework for addressing their everyday requirements. Maintaining accurate records to ensure the delivery of the care plan is reliant upon input from carers and managers. This human input will always be required, however automated audit trails provide a significantly greater level of protection.

Monitoring or intrusion?

Tagging, tracking and the use of CCTV equipment to monitor are clearly not appropriate in every care home environment. However, appropriate automated monitoring will maintain both the safety and dignity of those it is designed to protect.

Burden of proof

During CQC inspections and investigations the onus is placed on the provider to demonstrate care procedures are both appropriate and correctly delivered. Unambiguous, automated, evidential based compliance reports are an invaluable aid to meeting this burden of proof.

Multiple site monitoring

The ability for multiple site operators to view data from all of their care homes is a recent innovation. When used in conjunction with routinely generated emailed reports, local and head-office management are kept aware of any potential issues.

Protecting reputations

During the investigation of specific events or complaints, or during disciplinary hearings, recorded monitoring can often prove indispensable in protecting the reputation of individuals and businesses against accusations of incompetence or neglect. It can also have the opposite effect.

"Better to have it and never need it than need it but not have it. The value of automated monitoring is clearly demonstrated when evidence is critical."

Help setting funding applications

Logging information from the nurse call system can be used to measure an individual's call frequency and time spent on both scheduled and unscheduled care provision. Over time this audit trail can provide evidence of increasing care provision requirements, and help set the appropriate funding level for a service user.

Competitive edge

In a competitive environment any advantage is welcome. Automatic documentation of an individual's care provides reassurance and peace of mind to the family of potential clients. Consider whether your quality logging technology can be used to help keep your bed spaces full.

The final analysis

Forewarned is very definitely forearmed and the ability to quickly identify falling standards in a care home gives you and your senior management the early warning they need to address issues before they become legal or financial risks, or a physical risk to the wellbeing of residents.

Are you sure you are handing out pills safely?

TERESA LYNSKEY

founded Lynskeys Care Services Consultancy having spent 15 years working in the care sector with leading companies, and is a trustee of the Care Professionals Benevolent Fund.

In the care home sector more complex drug treatments and significant growth in co-morbidity are placing increasing demands on staff. Medicines management has been the area of most concern across the different types of social care services (*CQC market report June 2012*). This report highlighted that the area of highest non-compliance was the "management of medicines". Problems identified included the administration of medicines not being properly recorded, and policies and procedures not being followed by all staff. It should be emphasised that compliance with the essential standards in the management of medicines is required by law.

'Five Rights'

Before a nurse or any other healthcare professional gives a medication in a care home the "five rights" questions should be asked: "Is this the **right** dose of the **right** medication given to the **right** patient in the **right** way at the **right** time?"

Supporting clients with medication

Young people, frail older people, people with a physical disability or learning disabilities, to name just a few, will all have their own unique needs, abilities and requirements for different types of support with medication. All this must be agreed with the client, recorded in the care plan and reviewed regularly. Eighty per cent of people in care homes have dementia or severe memory problems (*Alzheimer's Society*) and must feel respected and valued. The same applies when it comes to medication – take the time to communicate and understand for example if they are in pain and need their *prn* paracetamol.

'One medicine' for 'One person'

It may be tempting for staff to give medicines intended for another resident to a resident whose stocks may have run out. However, legally, medication prescribed for an individual belongs to that person alone and should never be given to another, even if they are both on the same medicine. Medicines must always be administered from their original container or bottles in which they were dispensed by the pharmacy. This includes all compliance aids.

Ordering prescriptions on time

One study shows that 49.1% of all medicine administration errors in care homes were clients missing doses (*CHUM study, Barber et al. 2009*). This can sometimes be caused by staff not allowing the up to 14-21 days needed to order and receive prescription medicines.

Creating an audit trail

Care homes are legally obliged to record all medicines received, administered, returned or disposed of, on the medication administration record (MAR) whether paper-based or electronic. Create an audit trail by always checking and verifying the quantity received, and that the entry is dated and initialled by the person checking it.

Errors in medication administration

The results of medication errors can be damaging to both resident and care worker. Errors need to be documented; the prescriber informed and policies and procedures implemented including liaising with the resident and, as appropriate, with relatives.

Patient Information Leaflets (PILs) are worth reading

It is important to understand how drugs work and interact within the body. Always note the possible side effects and interactions listed on the patient information leaflets, and actively watch for any side effects or changes observed in your clients. PILs also list the contents of medication to help religious and cultural preferences to be respected.

"For it may safely be said, not that the habit of ready and correct observation will by itself make us useful nurses, but that without it we shall be useless with all our devotion."

– Florence Nightingale

Recognising side effects

Most medicines can cause side effects, but they won't occur in everyone. Common symptoms include restlessness, dizziness, nausea, confusion, diarrhoea, drowsiness and rashes. Any potential side effects must be reported to the person in charge and the prescriber informed. If a client has an anaphylactic reaction, don't hesitate, call an ambulance.

Barcode Medication Administration System (BCMA)

This is designed to help the medication administration process, preventing inappropriate short cuts and saving time with drug ordering and stock control. Warnings, such as allergy checking, are automatically performed; dose checking and relevant clinical data are also accessible. The technology, if used properly, can reduce errors even before the client is reached.

Electronic Medication Administration Record (eMAR)

Computer-generated paper MARs and electronic medication administration records (eMARs) can both reduce the risk of handwriting, omission, and transcription errors. However, this technology is continually developing and the terminology can be confusing, so seek advice on the tried and tested eMAR & BCMA solutions available.

Preventing and controlling cross infections

HELENA LITTLE

is director of quality and service at the Abbeyfield Society, a voluntary organisation providing supported housing and care for older people to alleviate loneliness.

There is a national drive for agencies to work together to reduce the number of infections occurring in social and healthcare provider settings, where there is shared eating and living accommodation. Public concern about infections is considerable, and so it is important to reassure residents and their relatives that the setting is safe and clean and that effective preventative and control measures are in place. Infections are a major cause of serious or even life-threatening illness in older people, whose age and, in many cases, underlying medical conditions make them more susceptible. Some infections arise out of resistance to antibiotics; some are passed from person to person and others occur as seasonal outbreaks in local communities. The main routes of spread are: Inhalation, contact (through the skin), ingestion. It is paramount to infection control to ensure that best practice is in place in care homes. The key points below are guidance to what a manager of a home should be doing.

Make it somebody's job

Identify a lead person for infection prevention and control within the care or nursing home and delegate responsibility to help manage the prevention and control of infection policy and procedures. The same person should take the lead in supporting supervision and training; promoting standards and good practice; and co-ordinating and liaising with external specialist infection control agencies. Designate a lead person or team member to ensure equipment cleaning and decontamination systems are in place and are being followed.

Keep yourself informed

Have access to information and up-to-date contact details for suitably qualified and competent persons from your local community health services and authorities for advice on infection prevention and control. These should include: Local Health Protection Units, Consultant in Communicable Disease Control and/or Consultants in Health Protection, Health Protection Nurse, General Practitioner, Community Infection Prevention and Control Nurse, Environmental Health Officer. Make sure there is an up-to-date copy of the local Community Infection Control Policy available.

Risk assessments

Undertake infection prevention and control risk assessments with residents, and generically record actions taken to reduce or remove risks. Carry out infection prevention and control audits annually, or more frequently if required.

Make staff aware
Ensure that management arrangements, procedures, standards and good practice for the prevention and control of infection are implemented and followed by staff, volunteers and visitors. Ensure all staff are made aware of, have access to and understand the infection prevention and control policies and procedures and reporting requirements used in the home.

Be equipped
Maintain standards and procedures to ensure that the equipment used for care is clean and the environment is clean and safe. Provide adequate supplies of personal protective equipment and cleaning materials and supplies.

Training
Identify individual training needs and ensure that staff and volunteers are provided with instruction, supervision and training on infection prevention and control appropriate to their roles and responsibilities.

"So never lose an opportunity of urging a practical beginning, however small, for it is wonderful how often in such matters the mustard-seed germinates and roots itself."

– Florence Nightingale

Monitor
Routinely monitor and review infection prevention and control management systems, standards and practice.

Managing outbreaks
Establish systems for senior care staff to follow for reporting suspected outbreaks of infection to HPU's and line managers, and for implementing actions to reduce and control the risk of infection within the home.

Record and report
Provide reports on incidents and outbreaks of infection as part of routine reporting procedures.

DH Code of Practice
Complete an annual report on infection control for the care or nursing home. Ensure for reference there is in each home a copy of the *'DH Code of Practice for health and adult social care on the prevention and control of infections and related guidance.'*

Preventing falls

Humans began to fall as soon as we started 'standing on our own two feet'. In the UK more than 400,000 people attend A & E each year with suspected hip fracture following a fall. There is not a lot a care home manager can do about that, but on your own patch in the care home falls become an exciting area for you to make a difference. Brennan (2004) showed that falls are 2.9 times more common in care homes than in personal homes and hip fractures are 3.3 times more common.

Dr Richard Hawkins

trained as a doctor and worked as a surgeon for the NHS and then part-time for the charity Marie Stopes. In 1985 he co-founded Hawker Publications, a publisher with a particular interest in social care and dementia, and the publisher of Caring Times and the Journal of Dementia Care

A no-fault policy encourages honesty

The key to running a successful falls programme is to know how many falls are happening in your home. You may think you know but are your staff actually noting every single one? It may help to have a no-fault policy which encourages honesty.

A numbers game

"Do I have too many falls in my home?" is another difficult question because numbers will inevitably vary with the type of clients in the home. A recent American study (*Centers for Disease Control and Prevention, 2011*) suggested an average 100 bed nursing-home has 100 - 200 falls a year.

Hundreds of contributing factors

There are two main risks you have to address constantly: the risk associated with the care home, and the individual risk of falling. National Institute for Health and Care Excellence (NICE) (2004) has estimated that there may be more than 400 separate factors contributing to a fall. Good luck!

A falls prevention committee

A falls prevention committee works well for many homes. It must include the manager (or nothing will happen), and other vital staff such as head chef, registered nurse, maintenance staff, activities organiser and night staff (very important). The committee needs to make a point of communicating the lessons they have learnt from every fall.

Prevention is best

Perhaps one in three falls are due to the home environment. Single steps should be banned, they are lethal. The last step of a flight commonly causes a fall so ensure it is clean and the rim well marked. Good lighting is essential everywhere; lighting must be uniform as well because older eyes are slow to adjust to changes. Bad lighting is worse than none. Railings need to be clean and put in well thought-out places.

Hazards

Staff need to watch for anything which will trip residents, a common cause of falls. Something new or unusual can be their undoing, like new or rucked-up rugs, cushions, packaging, games left in the lounge, or balls brought by grandchildren. Residents can't lift their feet as high as they used to and, when falling, they find they cannot right themselves as quickly as they once could. Tiredness contributes to falls so place chairs along long corridors to encourage residents to rest. Slip hazards to avoid include rainwater, oil, dust and any spillages (e.g. in the toilet) which must be wiped away immediately. Bathrooms are very hazardous places. Encourage good footwear and discourage trailing clothes.

Risks and benefits

Each resident should have a risk assessment for falls carried out. This assessment will help decide how risks can be reduced, and also help when monitoring the resident's quality of life. To keep a resident in bed, for example, just because they could fall, would be unacceptable. That said, residents will vary in their attitude to risk and this must be recorded in their care plan.

"The word 'fall' comes from the Old English word 'feallen' which means to fall or die – a particularly poignant derivation given the outcome of so many falls in older people."

Is it the drugs?

Medication is an area which is likely to bear fruit. Tranquillisers, diuretics, heart failure and high blood pressure drugs can all cause difficulties with balance or dizziness. The aim is to reduce the number and dosage of drugs as much as possible, but sometimes the residents are simply under-treated and need higher dosages. Remember the important role of pain. Pain causes residents to fall and painkillers do too.

Desperate residents fall

Focus on all aspects of incontinence management. Residents often fall because they are desperate, getting up alone from a chair because their call has not been answered quickly or desperate to reach a badly positioned toilet or because they cannot open their clothing easily. Telecare products to alert staff can often prevent this type of preventable fall occurring.

Reasons for action

A good care manager will want to take action on falls for ethical reasons. And it will probably keep you out of a nasty legal case too.

Moving and handling residents safely

There are three main considerations involved in planning safe moving and handling requirements for your residents. Namely: Sufficient space for the resident as well as any equipment that is required plus the carer; appropriate equipment to ensure the comfort, safety and dignity of the resident and reduce the load on the carer and lastly, the correct working techniques used by well-trained and competent carers.

MANDY CLIFT

has worked for the commercial sector for many years on programmes and products aimed at reducing the incidence of musculoskeletal injuries in healthcare. She has also worked on the development and implementation of manual handling education tools and programmes, along with assessment tools which can be used to measure the safety of working practices in healthcare settings.

Making the right choices

When planning a care facility, making the right choices will determine the efficiency of the unit, as well as the quality of care that can be given in the future. Good planning will result in less dependent residents who maintain their mobility for as long as possible. Carers will suffer less musculoskeletal strains and injuries which will lead to a more efficient and safer environment.

Work with your architect

Talk to your architect about space, e.g. toilets should have 800mm on either side to give carers sufficient space to assist residents while maintaining a good working posture. To allow adequate working space the toilet should measure 2000mm x 22000mm.

How to make the right choices about equipment

The resident's mobility level is the key to choosing the appropriate equipment and use of an assessment tool (such as the ArjoHuntleigh Mobility Gallery) will help you select the right equipment to suit their needs. Always allow staff the opportunity to trial equipment before making purchasing decisions.

Always choose height adjustability

Residents who can no longer carry out all their own daily care will require assistance from carers. Height adjustable equipment should always be selected to protect the carers from the risks of static overload. This rule applies to all necessary equipment such as beds, baths, shower systems etc.

Plan for changes over time

Residents' needs change as they get older and it makes sense to anticipate their require-ments when choosing equipment. For example, consider choosing a bathing system that is suitable for residents who have sitting balance in addition to a system for more dependent residents. A selection of systems rather than several all of the same type will ensure the residents' needs can be met.

Safety first

When choosing equipment, pay particular attention to the features that protect the safety, comfort and dignity of the resident. In general, higher quality equipment will have a better specification than cheaper equivalents and also give more years of service.

Flooring

The preferred option in a care setting is smooth, hard flooring that is easy to keep clean and allows wheeled equipment to be pushed without excessive effort rather than carpets. Maintaining daily hygiene and cleaning up spills is also much easier with hard flooring.

How much equipment?

As a rough rule of thumb mobile lifters should be allowed for on a one-to-ten ratio. That is, for example, one active lifter (standing and raising aid) should be allowed for each resident who requires assistance for transfers and toileting but has some ability to weight-bear. One passive sling lifter should be allowed for every ten residents without any weight-bearing ability.

"The care that nurses are able to deliver is only as good as the working environment in which they function."

– PROFESSOR ALAN GLASPER, PROFESSOR OF NURSING, UNIVERSITY OF SOUTHAMPTON

Ensure good working techniques

Educating carers on the principles of safe moving and handling and giving them sufficient time to practise their skills and knowledge will pay dividends – not just in the quality of care they can give to residents but also in protecting their own safety and wellbeing.

The bed

A height adjustable, profiling bed will provide the best level of support for residents of all dependency levels. Beds should be used in conjunction with appropriate therapeutic surfaces and handling equipment to give the resident optimum pressure area care.

Preparing food safely

The food and beverage service offered to residents in our 47-bed residential/dementia home not only meets the basic requirements, but excels. All legal and food safety regulation are met by using a process to eliminate risk of contamination, and by providing a safe menu for the different times of the day. Menus are set to include local fresh products, minimising processed foods by using catering skills to make food colourful and appetizing and non-cluttered. Our food is simple, easily identified and enjoyable as part of life in care.

JOANNE CANNISTER

is a kitchen manager with Ideal Care Homes. Joanne has worked in local authority and private care homes for the past 30 years.

Space/equipment

A kitchen must be sufficiently spacious to allow its different functions to be completed with safety and efficiency. There must be space for ambient, chilled and frozen storage. Equipment includes wash hand basins with soap & towels, a fry grill roast, steamer, dry and wet prep areas, a sink and dishwasher. It must be well-ventilated, well-lit and have provision for waste disposal.

Kitchen staff

Everyone working in the kitchen must be trained in kithen skills, personal hygiene, diet knowledge, be flexible and have personal involvement with residents' food needs. Serving staff should ensure meals are covered until served, and understand potential risks associated with different food types. They should assisting residents where necessary, and not rush the service. Staff should gather and report feedback form residents on the quality of the meals and service.

Menus

When planning menus, staff should include the "five a day" principle when choosing fruit and vegetable portions. Where possible, locally-sourced, fresh ingredients should be used. Consideration should be given to providing regional menus that are understood by the residents.

Preparation

While working to timescales, the first rule is one job at a time, then clear and clean as you go. When preparing food, remember the required quantity and the rules regarding time, temperatures, cross-contamination and above all, remember to segregate cooked and raw items at all times.

Cooking

When planning out the day's kitchen activities, allow time for all foods to be cooked to the required temperatures and plan to minimise the time between the food being cooked and served to keep food safe and appetising. Again, care with chilled and ambient foods is essential to reduce the risk of contamination.

Serving

Mealtimes are an important social activity for residents and help to create a sense of routine. Staff should do their best to make each meal an enjoyable occasion for each resident.

Plate layout

People eat with their eyes by using colours, so three items on a plate is good and five items is excellent. Where possible food should be arranged to give the most colour contrast. Protein being particularly important in any diet is best placed at 6 o'clock on the plate directly in front of the resident. Take care with the resident's method of eating, whether this be with knife and fork, a spoon or with fingers.

"I enjoy making a difference with our food."

Ordering

Once residents have made their menu choices for the days ahead, it is then essential for the caterer to ensure that sufficient quantities of ingredients are available.

Parties and other events

Birthdays and anniversaries are very important for many older people and they are a wonderful opportunity to do something different to the normal mealtime routine. Buffets, barbecues and 'themed' meals are just some of the options.

Effective steps to preventing abuse taking place

SIMON HARRISON

is a nurse and professional interim director who works with organisations to ensure effective, efficient and economic delivery through implementation of strategic, operational and organisational change.

The Panorama programme of 2011 exposed abusive practices taking place at Winterbourne View. A series of investigations, reports and recommendations have rightly followed regarding the need for change. The Serious Case Review highlighted areas for improvement for providers, commissioners and regulators. When I started with Castlebeck as interim chief operating officer in January 2012, I knew I had a tough job ahead but my aim was to ensure we had the correct ABC (Attitude, Behaviour and Culture) and to ensure that the care we provided was safe, sound and supportive.

The first priority

Delivering a higher standard of care has to be the number one priority and the only way a business can work correctly. This can only be achieved if you have the right quality of staff at all levels through the organisation. This really does mean every single person, including you.

Passion at the heart of it

Ensure that at the heart of what you do there is a passion to make a difference to people and their families by delivering personalised health and social care that helps them achieve what they want out of life.

Everyone's responsibility

All staff have a role to play in enhancing the reputation of the business and in showing pride in their work. It is everyone's responsibility to carry a positive culture and change it where this is not observed.

Codes of conduct

Each professional discipline has its own code of conduct and standards of professional practice that must be followed. Staff need to be acutely aware of what this means for them (e.g. nurses).

Policies

Each employer must have a set of codes and policies within which all employees should be required to work. This must include respect for the people we care for.

Appraisal and supervision

The quality of day-to-day delivery of services relies on the performance of the staff we employ. Through robust appraisal and supervision we must ensure that every one of our staff are clear about their personal contribution to the achievement of high quality care.

Common goals and aspirations

Achieve a collective understanding of what "good" looks like. This includes asking those we care for. Services must be ever improving, never complacent.

Facilitate whistleblowing

Ensure there is a whistleblowing policy in place. All staff members at one time or another have concerns about what is happening at work. Usually these concerns are easily resolved. However, when you are troubled about something that involves a danger or risk (to service users, the public or colleagues), professional misconduct or financial malpractice, it can be difficult to know what to do. You may be worried about raising such an issue, perhaps feeling it's none of your business or that maybe it's only a suspicion. You may feel that raising the matter would be disloyal to colleagues, to managers or to the company. You may have said something but found that you have spoken to the wrong person or raised the issue in the wrong way and are not sure what, if anything, to do next. This policy must enable everyone to blow the whistle safely so that such issues are raised at an early stage and in the right way.

"Whenever you do a thing, act as though all the world were watching."

– Thomas Jefferson

Robust monitoring...

Ensure there are robust governance systems and processes in place and sound reporting systems and ensure all reports are analysed and trends identified.

... at all times

Be visible as a management team. That means out of hours and weekends.

Safeguarding adults at risk of abuse

LYNNE PHAIR

is an independent consultant nurse and expert witness working in adult safeguarding and specialising in investigating neglect of frail older people.

Safeguarding adults at risk must begin with how we, as care providers work, act and behave in our everyday practice. As leaders we must show how we prevent abuse in everything we do. The 10 points for safeguarding, are my moral compass; if leaders strive for these in themselves, others will follow, and the culture of care in teams, departments and organisations will be stronger, safer and more fulfilling for everyone. Here are the 10 points of my moral compass:

Trust

Users of services and their families must be able to trust an organisation to investigate their concerns fairly and openly. Just think how you would want your complaint investigated. Use your own desire for fairness, and value the needs of the complainant for justice as an equal to your own expectations.

Integrity

Believe in yourself and your role to protect those who cannot protect themselves. Be true to yourself, and work to serve those at risk as you would want to be served. Stand up for what you believe in and what you know to be right for your client.

Care and compassion

Care and compassion is at the heart of everything a care professional does. This means getting close to individuals so that care can be offered to help and comfort. Either when caring yourself or supervising others, celebrate the smallest things that can make the biggest difference to a person feeling safe, "loved" and cared for.

The dangers of group-think

Team decisions should involve everyone but you may not want to say the obvious for fear of looking silly. This is group-think. Everyone follows the herd, and that is when things go wrong. Say what you believe to be true, and sleep easy at night.

Mitigation not justification

Do not allow yourself to be sucked into feeling sorry for staff who neglected a client because of a problem with staffing, or training, or poor documentation. The reason something happened will affect the sanctions or consequences for the staff or organisation, don't allow it to justify what happened.

Caring is a privilege not a right

Having professional registration is the license that enables care workers to practice. Care should be given according to the rules, just like we can only drive a car according to the highway code. If we don't practice according to the rules we must accept responsibility and face the consequences.

Be proud of your profession

Be proud of what you do and speak up for what is right for clients. Use your head, your heart and your hands in everything you do. By being proud about what you represent you will not allow abusive practice destroy the lives of others.

Case Study

A daughter tried to find out why her mother died of pressure sores in a mental health hospital, but the hospital said it was part of her condition.

At the inquest the neglect was exposed. The daughter said to me: "Thank you, you gave a voice to someone who could not be heard."

Smarter staff selection

Use sound recruitment procedures, listen and watch the candidate carefully and trust your intuition. Ask clients or their families to interview too. They will not be worried about filling the vacancy, and will help you to be true to your beliefs and not be side-tracked by staff shortages.

Take care of the small concerns

Listen to concerns about small things that are not quite right. Think of them in the context of the culture of care, not simply as isolated issues. Be proportionate in your response, but be mindful of what a small concern could be hiding underneath.

Investigate, but be thorough and fair

Staff need to feel you will be fair, objective and open. Ensure they see any reports and have a chance to respond. Don't judge them before the facts are known, but be true to your own values and safeguarding of those at risk.

Issues you must not forget when insuring your care home

SUSAN LEE

was appointed managing director of Towergate Patrick in 2009, having joined Towergate in 2004. Susan has worked in the insurance business for more than 20 years.

With the commercial and regulatory environment changing all the time, running a care home can be complicated and demanding. Add to this a stream of negative publicity and the claim-friendly legal environment and it's increasingly likely you'll need to call on your insurance to deal with an allegation of wrong doing. Claims have the potential to cause serious financial and reputational damage but making sure you have the right cover in place is just the beginning. Access to specialist advice and business support is critical in helping you take a proactive approach to your legal liabilities and offers numerous additional benefits.

Use a care specialist

Every care home is unique, so you should work with an insurance broker who understands your particular operation and the wider challenges the care sector presents. Opt for a broker offering tailored packages that match cover with your specific needs.

Understanding the sector

The care industry is facing some serious challenges so it's advisable to work with an insurance broker with care sector underwriting and claims expertise in-house. They should be able to provide practical risk management advice to help lessen the likelihood and/or impact of claims made against you.

Know what you're paying for

What cover do you have in place? Is it keeping pace with your needs? In addition to standard property and liability covers, consider protection for your lost revenue in the event of licence suspension and cover for your directors and officers.

Keep your insurer informed

Your insurer needs to know about changes to your business including fluctuations in turnover or amendments to your sums insured. Remember to tell them about all the activities you organise including day trips and fêtes and check your Public Liability policy covers them all.

Legal help and expertise

As experts in care you'll need some specialist legal advice every now and then. Making sure your insurance package includes a care-specific legal helpline and adequate legal expenses cover can save a lot of unnecessary time, worry and expense.

Human resources software

Managing your workforce can be time-consuming especially given the continual changes in legislation. Choose an up-to-the minute, care-specific HR tool for access to the latest legal and regulatory information, best practice guidelines and template documentation. Some policies include this valuable feature for no additional cost.

Stress management

The care sector is vulnerable to high levels of stress among its workforce. Employers have an enduring responsibility to manage this issue carefully and responsibly so choose an insurance policy that includes a free, confidential stress helpline.

"As insurers we're here to pick up the pieces when things go wrong so we take a positive view of those care home managers that try to prevent problems happening in the first place, through robust risk management practices, and keep us informed about changes to their business."

– Jason Claydon, Fusion Insurance, part of the Towergate Group

Insurer stability

At its most basic an insurance policy is a promise to pay money (in defined circumstances) so you should be confident of your insurer's ability to do exactly that. Your broker can provide details of your insurer's financial strength and current credit rating.

Accident reporting

Working with an insurance broker experienced in dealing with claims reporting procedures can help reduce the risk of breaching policy provisions and cover being denied. A specialist will help you to prepare a robust defence and manage tight deadlines, assisting you through the process from beginning to end.

Take a long-term view

The recent rise in claims has resulted in premium increases and made it difficult for some care homes to obtain cover at all. Building a long-term relationship with an insurance specialist will help you get the protection you need as your business develops and grows.

7

Staff: Your most valuable resource

Recruiting the best staff

SUSAN BAVERSTOCK

is group head of human resources and training at the Somerset Care Group, with 20 years experience across all aspects of strategic HR management.

In a sector where staffing costs are your single highest overhead, the importance of recruiting and retaining the right staff is essential to the success of your business. Ensuring that you employ staff with the right skills, attributes and attitudes is a key factor in your ability to deliver a quality service. Hard-won reputations are easily lost as a result of poor quality staff, so the importance of getting it right when recruiting cannot be over emphasised. The following 10 tips should assist you with making sure that you make the right decisions.

It's all about reputation

What attracts someone to apply in the first place? Company reputation is an important factor to attracting good quality candidates. Don't miss opportunities to promote your care home or company and maximise good news stories. Those interested in working for a quality organisation or looking to develop a career in care will want to work for quality providers.

Consider your recruitment options

Newspaper advertising can be costly – try using banner- lines to direct applicants to your website. While cheaper, this gives you the opportunity to use your website to promote a really positive picture of your company. "Talking Heads" on your site can provide an insight into the working life of a carer. Word of mouth is also a very effective recruitment method, using an "Introduce a Friend" bonus to incentivise current employees.

Be thorough – mind the gaps!

Follow up any gaps in the chronology of an applicant's employment history. It may just be an oversight but they may be hiding something!

The importance of attitude and values

In the care sector, attracting staff with the right attitudes and values is key. Consider using an appropriate on-line tool to test these areas before applicants are selected for interview. Also, ensure that interview questions ask for examples to demonstrate behaviours in different situations.

Choose your interviewers carefully

Make sure those interviewing have received appropriate training to equip them, e.g. using probing questions and scenarios to ensure interviews are thorough. Also, applicants will make judgements about the company based on how interviewers conduct themselves.

The resident's perspective

Always ensure that you observe how applicants interact with residents as part of the interview process. Do they demonstrate the right behaviours and approach? Listen to resident feedback – it's essential.

The realistic picture

Especially where applicants are new to care, ensure they have a realistic understanding of all the job entails. Underplaying more challenging areas may result in their leaving in the early days if they aren't prepared for the realities of the role.

Promoting care as a career

Promoting opportunities for development for new staff is key. Not all applicants will be looking for future promotions but most will value a chance to maximise their own potential. Giving examples of staff who have progressed through the organisation will show how it values and invests in its staff.

"I am convinced that nothing we do is more important than hiring and developing people. At the end of the day you bet on people, not on strategies."

– Lawrence Bossidy, former chief executive of General Electric and author

How flexible can you be?

Getting the balance is essential. Staff may be looking for shift patterns to fit with commitments but ensure that you align these with business needs. Constantly trying to meet individual requests can result in odd shifts left uncovered which are tricky to recruit to.

What if you make a mistake?

On occasion it may quickly become apparent that a new employee is not right for the post, despite training and support. If this occurs, take decisive action and end the employment in the probationary period. This is better for all concerned rather than allowing unsuitable employees to remain in post.

Retaining your staff

I t's a busy day and amid the other zillion things you have to do, the ominous envelope from a member of staff appears on your desk. Another resignation letter. It feels like staff are dropping like flies, and good replacements are like hen's teeth. How many care hours are you short now? How are you going to fix this? What's the secret to a low staff turnover? This important strategic issue is all too often subject to a quick fix. However, mastering the dark art of staff retention is absolutely vital and brings untold further benefits.

ROGER PRATAP

has run care homes since 1994. Roger founded leading luxury operator Majesticare. His expertise in finance, property and strategy has delivered strength, reputation and value.

Make staff retention your best friend

Recognise that retaining your staff is invaluable. It's not merely about recruitment costs or management time – the true impacts of staff turnover are on reputation, occupancy, agency staff usage, morale, more staff leaving – in fact conquer this one and suddenly life gets a whole lot easier.

The serious side to morale

Bonding activities have their place, but you also need a serious morale strategy. Low morale, poor quality of work, absenteeism and staff turnover tend to feed off one another. Respect, value and appreciate your staff – this costs nothing but to them it is as valuable as their salary. Ask for input and give them a voice. Staff who are proud of their work and their employer are at their happiest, and they will stick with you.

Think it's all down to pay?

Your rates of pay can't always be the best, but research has proven the best people often stay for non-monetary rewards. Care about your staff and support them – personally and professionally. Their wellbeing and job satisfaction feeds the reputation of the home and keeps them by your side.

Recruit recruit!

A few people leave and everyone is working extras to plug the gap. Worse still, you have agency staff. Positions made vacant create workload for those who are left, which snowballs as the good people left behind grow frustrated with overwork, uninterested co-workers and instability. Always know your shortage of contracted hours, and recruit!

Why the best staff stay (or go)

The most caring staff will stick to a job where they work with other caring staff. They want to be surrounded by quality and good practice, and supported by an organisation committed to the same values as them. So quality breeds quality.

Leadership and loyalty

If you fail to lead your home, your talented staff will seek leadership elsewhere. Leadership is much more than instructing and directing people. Your emotional strengths, behavioural characteristics, standard setting, integrity and commitment are what build your team's loyalty.

Communicate and empower

People who feel they are making a difference will stick to their jobs, but those who feel their views don't matter will behave like 'hired hands' and will leave on a whim. Give plenty of feedback to your staff, recognise their potential, train them well, then give them autonomy.

Negativity doesn't work

Learn to put the right spin on negative feedback – criticise constructively! Be fair, be consistent and be nice. "I praise loudly. I blame softly." (*Catherine the Great, 1729-1796.*)

"The scholar does not consider gold and jade to be precious treasures, but loyalty and good faith."

– CONFUCIUS (*551-479*)

A sense of purpose

Paying attention to staff retention shapes the culture of your care home and develops a collective sense of purpose for all the staff. This cultural shift leads to greater focus on the residents. Staff feel like valuable individuals with unique skills. Then they truly become the single most valuable part of the business.

Bad staff or bad manager?

To finish with the words of Jean Paul Getty: "The employer generally gets the employees he deserves".

Motivating your team

AVNISH GOYAL

is the chief executive of Hallmark Care Homes, operating 18 high quality care homes and has a passion for helping people to achieve their full potential.

W e often hear organisations say "our people are our greatest asset" but do we ensure that this is not just rhetoric and that our teams actually feel this to be the case every day? When people feel motivated they naturally demonstrate enhanced performance and the need for fewer controls and procedures becomes evident; all of which ultimately makes a great business case. Creating a culture where people feel motivated and valued has to start from the top and needs to be inculcated right the way through to all parts of the organisation down to team members in the front line. Here are 10 points that support motivating your team.

Clear vision

Do you, as manager, have a clear vision as to where your company is heading and has this been communicated to all members of the team, including new members, as part of their induction? The vision should be inspiring, believable and achievable.

Values

Does the company have values that are developed with the people that work there, acting as a compass to help guide the company towards their vision? These values should be inculcated throughout the organisation to become part of the culture. They need to be demonstrated day in, day out by you as a leader, especially during tough times.

Recruitment

How does the organisation recruit the right people into the right roles? Are there appropriate job description and person specifications for all the roles and how is the attitude of a candidate as well as their aptitude being measured? Does the company use assessment days as part of their recruitment and selection process to ensure the 'right fit'?

Induction

How is the 'on boarding experience' for new recruits? Is there a robust induction to support and guide the new recruit through their first few weeks? A 'buddy' system allows the new recruit to have someone they can go to and ask questions to enable them to settle in.

Performance management

Does the employee know what success looks like? In other words have they been set 'SMART' objectives (Specific, Measurable, Attainable, Relevant and Time-bound) and do they have regular meetings with their line manager where there is an exchange of information as well as a discussion on strengths and areas for development? Are career opportunities discussed at these meetings?

Fair deal

Do team members feel that they are being paid fairly for the job compared to others in the company with the same role? Are the rates of pay competitive within the locality or the sector? What are the other benefits attached to the job that create a 'feel good' factor?

Resources

Does your organisation invest in the right resources for the employee to do the job to the best of their ability? The team need the right equipment, training and allocation of time to do the job effectively.

"Everyone knows success in ten pin bowling is a strike, ie knocking all the pins down in one go. Do team members know what a 'strike' looks like for them in their role? So that they know when they have done a good job and can get praised for it as well as celebrate their achievements?"

Acknowledgements

Is there a culture of catching people doing things wrong or is the culture to accentuate the positive by catching people doing things well? Are employees praised and recognised for doing good work? Is praise timely and specific and not just at formal meetings?

Listening

Do you as a manager listen and take feedback? Employees should feel that their opinions count and that they can make a difference to the organisation.

Feedback

Does the feedback received make a difference? When employees give feedback this needs to be acted upon by you and the rest of the management team and these actions communicated back to the team on a timely basis so that they can see the changes.

Making staff training effective

The days of minimal training in the care sector have gone and there is now a regulated structure for ensuring that people who use our care services are supported by care workers who are knowledgeable and skilled in the regulated activities they are providing. With a national training framework of qualifications to support this, there is every opportunity for raising the reputation for excellence in care from an informed and effective workforce. However, training on its own will never be sufficient and there needs to be a commitment from managers to effectively supervise and support care workers to put into practice what they have learned.

JACKIE POOL

is chief executive of Jackie Pool Associates Ltd, providing dementia care training services and materials and author of the Skills for Care QCF dementia units.

A key part of the business plan

View training as a worthwhile investment. Workforce development should result in a reputation for skilled and compassionate care and so be a key part of the business plan for achieving your business goals for good occupancy levels and low staff turnover or absences.

Establish what is needed

Identify what training your workforce members need in order to deliver a high quality service. Use the Skills for Care Skill Selector Tool (http://skillselector.skillsforcare.org.uk) for building qualifications that are mapped to the QCF framework and identifying learning opportunities that are right for your organisation.

Check-out your trainer

Remember, you get what you pay for! Good training costs more because the trainer has invested in their own continuing development, has public liability and professional indemnity insurance and has their own supervision system to ensure their own quality. Ask the trainer for evidence of these.

Measure the outcomes

Provide the trainer with details of what you want your workforce to be able to do after they have participated in the training. Learning should result in workforce practice development, not just workforce knowledge development. Measure the outcomes in terms of the impact on the individuals who use your service and on your workforce confidence and morale.

Be prepared to adapt

Be ready to support your workforce to translate their learning into care practice. Ensure that you are prepared to change your systems, routines, procedures and practice to develop your service in line with new learning and new ways of thinking.

Participate

Don't just send your workforce on the course – go on the course with them. Knowing what is being learned means that you can support translation into practice. You can monitor the quality of the training service and you can create a whole team approach where everyone is sharing the learning experience.

Share the learning with the entire team

View your workforce as everyone in your team and not only those who have a job description for providing care. Shared learning not only builds the team, it also supports everyone who may interact with a resident to understand the experience of living with dementia for eample.

"Good work requires excellence, ethics and engagement. If any one of these is missing there will always be a compromise on the work being delivered."

– HOWARD GARDNER (2009) FIVE MINDS FOR THE FUTURE, HARVARD BUSINESS SCHOOL PRESS

Identify further training needs

Ensure that your supervision methods support the team to deliver the care practices that they have learned. Supervision can be used to gather outcome measures of the success of the training event and to support the team, recognising and valuing team members' development and also identifying further training needs.

What do residents think?

Find out from residents how the training has impacted on them – observe their responses to team members' actions and interactions and also ask them for their opinions about the service they are receiving.

A continuing process

Plan a continuous cycle of training for the team. Training should not be a one-off event but should support an ethos of continuing professional development for all.

Volunteering in care homes

Volunteers provide immense value to our charity and the older people we support. From practical support to befriending and activities, our volunteers support older people to lead fulfilled lives. Attitudes towards volunteering in care homes can vary; from "we couldn't do without them" to "they're just a management headache". Actually, both of these statements can contain the seeds of failure. If we recruit volunteers to reduce costs, in particular replacing staff, we can become too reliant on them. But, if we see them as a management headache, we are unlikely to make them integral to our care home teams. There are huge benefits to having a range of volunteers in care homes and, when successful, volunteering brings real benefits to all. So how can you achieve success?

RICHARD FURZE

is chief executive of Friends of the Elderly.

Be very clear what you need from your volunteers

The more specific you can be about your volunteer roles the better. Start by looking at what will add the most value to your home and then create simple role descriptions. Make sure that all staff know what each volunteer's role is and welcomes them into the team.

Play to the volunteer's own strengths and needs

Some people may be brilliant befrienders, have a useful talent or skill they can share or enjoy administration. Remember to be flexible, allowing for those who can commit several hours to those who can only help out in school holidays. We need to think "flexiteering"!

See volunteers as part of your overall support team

Look at the care plans for each resident and match up what volunteers can add to enhance their support and care. Some residents will enjoy group activities but others much prefer to spend time one-to-one. Your volunteers can help you provide this extra flexibility.

Encourage volunteers to bring the community into the home

Residents need to have opportunities to remain engaged with their local communities. Why not encourage volunteers to run clubs and activities for the benefit of the wider community in which residents can participate? Support volunteers who want to organise outings by dealing with the practicalities around risk assessments, driver insurance and the like.

Be clear who has management responsibility for volunteers

Make sure each volunteer is clear about who they report to and where to go for support and guidance. This doesn't have to be the management team, it could be an ideal opportunity for staff to develop their leadership and mentoring skills.

Get connected locally

There are many ways to find volunteers and most will be very local; try your volunteer bureaux, library, schools, colleges and faith groups. But also think about local sheltered housing schemes or approaching staff in local businesses. You may be surprised that people respond well to being asked.

Never underestimate the importance of induction

Volunteers, like staff, need a thorough induction into the care home, its values and ethos and the role they will undertake. If they are working with people with particular needs such as dementia or poor hearing or communication, don't underestimate their training and support needs.

"I loved speaking with those young volunteers. They talked to me as if I was twenty again, I had to tell them I'm ninety!"

– MARY, A RESIDENT

Case History

John lived in a local sheltered housing scheme and regularly popped in to visit with some of our residents. After his wife Betty died, we noticed John was visiting more often and spending time with any resident who was around. We asked John if he would be interested in being a volunteer. Now, he runs the afternoon tea trolley chatting to each and every resident as he goes, bringing a smile to all – especially those with few visitors. John says "coming into the home gives me something that makes me feel worthwhile".

Use plain English

You should have good policies and procedures for volunteering – but make sure they are written in plain English and are easily understandable. While good processes and policies are needed – do make sure they are empowering and motivating rather than off-putting.

Don't forget to say thank you

Don't underestimate the value of a thank you. Invite volunteers to team meetings and relevant events and include them in internal communications. Why not have a special party, just for them, once a year? Residents will also enjoy thanking and honouring them.

8
Getting personal

Secrets of how to impress in interviews

Given that your career is likely to be the next most important thing outside of family, I'm continually amazed by the apathetic way in which a large number of candidates approach the interview. Lateness or tardiness is, in the main, unacceptable; why apply further pressure to an already pressured situation? As an experienced recruiter I've had the misfortune of witnessing many a candidate disintegrate in front of me – I've heard every excuse for untimeliness and poor performance and attribute the majority to a lack of planning. So here are my top 10 tips to help successfully navigate the interview – good luck!

ADAM CARTER

With 17 years' market exposure, Adam is recognised as one of the most knowledgeable recruiters within the independent care sector and a trusted advisor to care organisations and investors.

Know where you're going

I know it's obvious but pick up the phone in advance and ask! En route to the interview is not the ideal time to discover that car park availability is limited or it's a ten minute walk from the tube or train station.

Do your research

You are certain to be asked specific questions about the company, so make sure you've done your homework – you'll find financial data at Companies House or the Charity Commission; the company website will outline operational scale, key personal and corporate mission statement; and the Care Quality Commission is the perfect place for the regulator's view of a care home – you might also seek to 'mystery shop'.

Know who you are

You should know your strengths and weaknesses – understanding your weaknesses is a strength and demonstrating what you're doing to address these shows insight.

Know your business

There's no better way of demonstrating your commercial prowess than by performing a quick 'SWOT' analysis of your care home – Strengths, Weaknesses, Opportunities and Treats. In addition – know your numbers – staff, turnover, fees, etc.

Practice your answers

Anticipating some of the questions they might ask and rehearsing your answers is an easy way to calm the nerves – present your successes and evidence how you overcame failures. This adds colour to your answers and gives the interviewer some idea of the type of person you are, but don't be too prescriptive, a decent recruiter will spot the script and take you off-piste to catch you out.

First impressions count

Be confident but not arrogant and dress appropriately – the plain fact is that you are often judged before you've even uttered a word. While we all embrace individuality, the interview is not the place for self-indulgent expression. If you're unsure, check with the potential employer – most companies have a dress code policy.

Say what you mean

Think about your answers and do not just blurt out a response. Just take your time and even if an answer is not immediately forthcoming, buy some time by saying something like, "Let me think about that" – a well-thought-out answer is much better than one without any thought at all.

"We are what we repeatedly do; excellence, then, is not an act but a habit..."

– ARISTOTLE

Ask questions

Prepare a minimum of five questions that demonstrate your interest in the position.

Beware the recruiters' killer question

As day becomes night, you can be sure that any positive question I ask will swiftly be followed by a negative one – "what is the best commercial decision you've made" is quickly followed by "the worst" – nearly every candidate is caught off-guard and then in a panic, overcompensates with enough information to unlock any career skeletons – be aware.

Be prepared for a competency-based interview

While historically this 'balanced scorecard' approach was used by HR functions, increasingly recruiters use this interview technique. Questioning requires you to evidence through your career experience that you have the skills required to do the job – be prepared.

Getting off to a good start as a manager

CAROLYNNE MILLER

is chief executive of Elizabeth Finn Homes where she has worked for the past nine years. She is passionate about delivering high quality care.

The first few weeks as a care home manager may be challenging and a little daunting. Most managers are nurses and understand the professional and care aspects, but are less familiar with other roles such as managing catering, housekeeping, maintenance, gardens and administration. Never underestimate the importance of knowing what to do if the boiler breaks down on a weekend! You are legally responsible as registered manager and fully accountable for everything in the home. Quality of care is the most important aspect and it has to be right first time, every time.

Understand your home

During your first days it is important that you absorb, observe and begin to understand the culture of the home, the individuals in it and the wider community. Residents, staff, visiting professionals, volunteers, families and friends interact daily and affect one another. You will undoubtedly spot things that you may wish to change, but hold fire until you understand the dynamics.

Calming the fears

Meet the residents and volunteers as soon as possible. They will be apprehensive about any change of management and what effect that will have on their lives. Listen to their concerns and offer reassurance. They will be interested to learn of your background and experience, need to feel you are professional and that they can approach you with any concerns. Afternoon tea on day one would be a great starting point.

Meet the staff

Meet with staff from every department as quickly as possible. Introduce yourself, talk about your career, experience and your plans and dreams for the home. Meet separately with your heads of department – these will be your right-hand men and women and their skills and abilities will be invaluable as you settle into your new role.

One big family

Arrange to meet families and friends. They will be worried at this major change and the effect it will have on the residents. They will need the opportunity to ask questions and to be reassured of your professionalism. Emphasise that your door is open for suggestions and discussion, but that you will take a little time to settle in. A cheese and wine event could be appropriate.

Listening skills

Your company's operations manager will be a key resource in understanding your home. They will know what the company expects, what issues are in the home currently and any important matters which need to be addressed urgently.

Money matters

Review your budgets, look at the latest Key Performance Indicators, and speak to the financial director. Set up regular meetings with your administrator to review income and expenditure – it is crucial that any difficulties are addressed promptly. You will need to quickly learn about the financial reporting systems.

Marketing

Keeping the beds full is a major part of the role, so an efficient sales and marketing strategy is vital. The importance of making links with key professionals who can assist, such as GPs and social workers, cannot be underestimated. Ensure that you set up systems to deal with enquiries, callbacks and visits and plan your sales route to show off the best of the home.

"I believe the real difference between success and failure in a corporation can be very often traced to the question of how well the organisation brings out the great energies and talents of its people."

— THOMAS J. WATSON, JR., *A BUSINESS AND ITS BELIEFS*

The small print

Read the policies and procedures – they are different in every organisation. Become familiar with regular reports, audits etc which you will need to complete and understand the timescale. Each company has its own care planning system which you will need to familiarise yourself with in order that you can make *ad hoc* checks to reassure yourself that all is functioning properly.

Quality check

Check the most up-to-date Care Quality Commission inspection report and your last internal audit report. Confirm that any actions have been addressed and if not, begin to formulate a plan to address matters. Internal audits must be read and questions asked if there are outstanding actions.

Making the link

If your home is part of a group, begin to make links with other managers. They can guide you through the formal and informal systems in the organisation and may tell you information 'off the record'. Remember, everyone has been in your position at some time in their career and come through it!

Becoming a great manager

JOHN BURTON

Starting in 1965, John Burton has worked and campaigned at all levels for better social care with people of all ages, mostly in residential care.

Managing a care home is a great job and it needs a great manager . . . like you! Great managers lead great homes, but, if your proprietor is half-hearted about running a great home, you're unlikely to succeed. You and your proprietor must put the care of residents above everything. Good care and feeling 'at home' are what make a great care home and are the only reason for a care home to exist. Sometimes, you may have to remind your employer that the best way to market your home is establishing and maintaining its reputation for good care and homeliness. Your job is on three levels: in the home, outside the home and beneath the surface. All are equally important.

Manage yourself first

Your principle resource for doing this job is yourself: your personality, your experience, your values, your energy and your attitude. You must understand yourself. Your resolve and resilience will be tested because, although it's a great job, it's not an easy one.

Do it your way

Dare to be different and refuse to go along with what you know to be wrong. When you do this, you will lead by example. You will communicate to your staff – and very possibly to the residents – that they too can say "No" when they are being asked to do something they shouldn't.

Take stock of the situation

When you start the job, you need to know what's happening and work out why it's happening. You can do that only by being there, working alongside staff and residents – early in the morning, at night, at weekends – and experiencing what they are experiencing, feeling what they are feeling. Only when you identify the roots of problems will you be able to lead radical change.

Create a vision and a story

Share them with the team and the residents . . . and the relatives, and those outside the home who will support the changes you are going to lead.

Manage your own time

Resist the pressure on you to work office hours. Everyone outside the home will expect you to be at their beck and call 9 to 5, Monday to Friday, but those hours represent less than a quarter of the working week of a care home and, even during office hours, there will be many calls on your time from staff and residents within the home.

Manage your own work

Try to have a routine for yourself and vary your work, leaving space for thinking! Make a habit of eating with the residents every day. Never eat in the office. Take ten minutes sitting or having a stroll in the garden with your cup of coffee. Carry a small notebook. Think, imagine, reflect, plan.

Your long-term plan is achieved in small steps

While thinking about the parts, never forget they are parts of a whole system: a change in one part affects all other parts. Change at one level affects each of the other two levels. Every change is a step in the overall direction you've set.

"Compliance carries with it a sense of futility for the individual and is associated with the idea that nothing matters and that life is not worth living."

– Donald Winnicott, Playing & Reality

Communicate by example and the spoken word

Yes, talk with people, and encourage others to talk together. Keep notices and memos to a minimum – they are poor ways to communicate and very good at giving the wrong message.

Push responsibility and decision-making downwards

When your staff are struggling with some aspect of the job, do it with them but never do it for them. Whenever possible, everyone in the home should take their own decisions.

Be reliable and surprising

Be determined and flexible; follow up changes; work hard; enjoy yourself and become a great manager!

Planning a career in the care sector

NYREE KIDD

is HR director at Elizabeth Finn Homes, where she has been for 11 years. She is extremely proud to work with so many wonderfully committed people.

Planning a career in management should ensure that you take opportunities that will give you the experience in the different management elements. Although first and foremost you must have a passion and commitment for the role and service, if you don't like change, developing others and achieving results through delegating responsibility then think again. Consider your own values – you may already be a nurse and passionate about care and independence of individuals, but are you equally enthusiastic about leading and inspiring others to develop their commitment and passion? Nurture these qualities in yourself, colleagues and staff.

Knowledge

Keep abreast of regulation and best practice. Ponder developments and explore this thinking with colleagues to develop quality improvements. This shows your interest in the progression of your service. Research and attain appropriate qualifications to enable your advancement, your employer may support you in this.

Leadership and management

As you look for promotion in your career, find opportunities to lead and manage others. You will need to be able to do both and they are different, so develop both of these competencies.

Step out of the comfort zone

You may feel confident in managing care teams as the qualities and requirements are familiar. Seek opportunities for managing other teams such as administrative, housekeeping, etc. This will help you learn different management styles for getting the best out of different teams.

Delegation and peace of mind

In management you are delegating responsibility. Gain experience in actively participating in audit processes and team meetings, giving considered and constructive feedback. You will need to rely on others in a management role, so get early exposure in gaining evidence of performance within your business.

Financial aspects

To develop into a manager you must get a grip on the finances. Seek opportunities or volunteer to manage sections of budgets and review your management accounts. There are 'Finance for non-financial managers' courses out there and they may give you confidence.

Computers and technology

There is nowhere to hide from technology. If your workplaces are paper-based, it's time to get your own computer. It is essential that you can produce Word and Excel documents, file them (and find them again!), along with email and internet search as the minimum expectation of IT competence.

Marketing, sales & occupancy

As manager you must ensure good occupancy, understanding the marketing and sales process. Hone your skills in taking telephone enquiries, get involved in meeting prospective clients, research the competition so you know your care home's strengths and weaknesses. Engage in activities at work or social life that evidence your capability and willingness to promote a service.

"Consult not your fears but your hopes and your dreams. Think not about your frustrations, but about your unfulfilled potential. Concern yourself not with what you tried and failed in, but with what it is still possible for you to do."

– POPE JOHN XXIII

Grooming and presentation

In achieving your career aspiration of manager you will need to 'walk the talk'. The home manager is the front-of-house role – be confident in your own performance and lead by example all of the time, your staff will thank you for it.

Achieving career progression

Keep brief records of your exposure and achievements in the examples above, you may have fantastic experience, yet forget about it when it comes to applying or interviewing for a position. Use records to refresh your memory prior to interviews – this will assist you with recall. As a manager you will be expected to have an opinion on regulation and practice, so prepare your thoughts in advance.

Don't give up

Things won't always go smoothly but stick with it. We learn from every experience, so if you've taken a wrong turn, learn from it and let it give you the drive to move forward.

Keeping up-to-date

DR TERRY TUCKER

is director of learning and organisational development at Barchester Healthcare. Terry's career has spanned hospitality, further education and the NHS. She was involved with Richards and Cavendish Reviews. Her doctorate was "Leadership Development and Complexity in Healthcare".

Keeping up-to-date seems an obvious thing to do. The problems highlighted in the Francis and Cavendish Reviews, the new NHS structure, being aware of IT solutions to problems, professional developments, the latest thinking in your area are all subjects, for example, with which you should be familiar. Yet once you are settled into your chosen career, you might take a deep sigh of relief, not realising that your learning journey is only just starting. Outlined below are some of the ways you can keep up-to-date which will enhance your credibility as a professional and encourage your teams to do the same.

Consult and discuss

Your professional reputation will be gained and maintained only when you are respected for your knowledge and ability. Being confident about current thinking in your field encourages others to consult and discuss issues with you, and this earns you professional credibility.

Find a mentor

Having a mentor will expose you to thinking and researching prior to your sessions, as well as the stretching conversations you can expect from your mentor. Choose your mentor for their knowledge and reputation rather than the status of their role.

Choose a study programme

Choosing the right study programme for you (not necessarily the cheapest one) among the myriad available requires research and care. Choose a reputable programme which will enable you to link academic study with your day-to-day role. Link in external seminars, conferences, meetings and workshops as appropriate. Add to the body of knowledge in the whole team by encouraging your team to keep up-to-date too.

Journals and websites

These will inform you of the latest thinking in your field to help you keep up-to-date. Do not be shy about contacting authors for more information or to discuss what they have written, the thinking behind the articles and what prompted them.

Keep up with technology

Your ability to use technology, as well as knowing what is available and how it's being used, could change how you work. There are great podcasts and blogs that can be extremely informative, while easy to access in short spaces of time.

Networking

Keep up-to-date with your care environment and what's happening around you. National and local groups could be useful to you, as well as knowing what's going on in the local community and who you need to develop a relationship with. Read local newspapers and join networking groups: they will help with environmental scanning.

Reflect on experience

Most of our learning is indirect, from the work we do; only a small amount comes from courses and programmes of study. Reflect on what you have done, how well you coped in difficult situations. What can you learn when things didn't go as planned? A reflective diary and clinical supervision are effective ways to identify and consolidate new learning.

Action Learning Sets

Join an Action Learning Set to accelerate your learning, hone your questioning skills and improve your ability to deal with real problems. A set member shares a problem or issue and the group helps that member to define the problem clearly and find a way forward, through skilful questioning. It takes place with a group of like-minded people and a skilled facilitator. You will learn from peers in an atmosphere of trust and openness.

Inspire confidence

Leadership isn't about having all the answers but knowing where to find them. Teams need confidence that their manager is up-to-date with current thinking, with their sector and the organisation they work for.

"We cannot teach people anything; we can only help them discover it within themselves."

– GALILEO GALILEI

Living a healthy lifestyle and working in care

DR RICHARD HAWKINS

trained as a doctor and worked as a surgeon for the NHS and then part-time for the charity Marie Stopes. In 1985 he co-founded Hawker Publications, a publisher with a particular interest in social care and dementia, and the publisher of Caring Times and the Journal of Dementia Care.

It might seem obvious that if we work in care, we should live a healthy lifestyle. The evidence, sadly, is the opposite. Carers have higher than average levels of alcoholism, drug abuse, backache, obesity, suicide and depression. Your staff's health is therefore at risk, and as a good manager you have a duty of care here. Your challenge is knowing where to draw the line between being 'supportive' and being 'interfering'. You are responsible for your own health too. Below are some of the scenarios you may encounter:

Manager: "If that man makes one more complaint, I'll scream"

Clear evidence here of a person under stress, the commonest negative scenario managers report. The likeliest causes are pressure due to an excessive workload, lack of control, interference by senior management, regulatory threats, complaints, lack of support and especially understaffing. The causes are all preventable and solvable by a responsible employer.

Staff member: "I love coming to work and making a difference"

Brilliant comment. Find out what the secret to their happiness is, spread the word, promise, encourage, reward, high five, laugh. It doesn't take much to raise levels of that much loved magical brain substance- monoamine.

Staff member: "I think I'll pop out and have a ciggie"

Oh dear. What to do? Some American hospitals have already solved this problem by refusing to employ smokers on pain of immediate dismissal if caught. Hopefully your company has a policy banning smoking close to the home, which you can enforce with zero tolerance. If not, it's still zero tolerance. Smoking has nothing going for it apart from heart disease, strokes and being linked with many cancers.

Manager: "Boy, that was a tough meeting. I deserve a couple of those biscuits Fred bought for us"

Obesity is common in nurses. A University of Maryland study showed more than half of American nurses were obese. Focus on eating well at work: encourage healthy presents, don't snack on junk foods, use a rota for joining resident meals, and learn from your chef.

Staff member: "Amazing, that's my third hangover this week"

Alcohol is a constant threat for care home staff. It bears repeating: the recommended weekly safe limit for women is 14 units per week where 1 unit is half a pint of beer, a small glass of wine or a pub measure of spirits. Encourage staff not to drink alcohol at all for one to two days in the week.

Manager: "I feel so tired I can hardly drag myself into work"
There could be physical causes so get yourself a check-up from your GP. Never forget the possibility of depression. Of course you might be exhausted and just need a break or a change.

Staff member: "I've bought a pedometer"
Great idea – they cost as little as £6 (double with a calorie counter). Change your staff's reluctance to take exercise. Try team charity runs/bike rides/mountain climbing. Subsidise sports and gym membership. Involve your senior management in competitions for everyone to see who are faster, higher, stronger! Encourage staff to join the residents' exercise classes or Tai-Chi – they'll love the participation.

Ethnic minority staff member: "Everyone's very kind but they never look me in the eye and want to know the real me"
Help all staff realise how difficult and lonely it can be living and working many miles from your homeland, and to appreciate that in a healthy home , everyone is equally valued and respected.

"If I had my way, I'd make health catching, instead of disease."
– Peter Ingersoll

"Health and cheerfulness mutually beget each other."
– Joseph Addison, 1772

Manager: "I sometimes think I see Jenny hurting one of our residents, Alice, who lives with dementia"
The truth is the manager probably knows Jenny is hurting Alice but she doesn't want to make a fuss. Part of being a healthy is being able to live with yourself, secure in the knowledge that you are sticking to your principles and values, whatever the cost sometimes.

Team: "We like it best when there is laughter in the home. Laughter is the best medicine"

Do I matter?

SHARON BLACKBURN

is policy and communications director for the National Care Forum (NCF), a strategic nurse leader in adult social care, passionate about people, their potential and quality, and expert in change management – both strategic and in practice.

Each day as a manager or care worker you give: emotionally; physically; intellectually; spiritually and socially, always putting the other person first. Being compassionate, showing respect, giving and restoring dignity, giving worth to the person you care for and work with. How often, however, do you wish the same values were attributed to you? Feeling isolated, low, tired or even burnt-out is common – you are not alone. There will be competing priorities both in and outside of work: knowing what to do and how to handle how you feel and who to go to will be explored in the following points.

Stop

Be honest with yourself about how you are thinking and feeling. Question how is this making you behave? Take stock of where you are at. To be effective, knowing yourself is important. It is very easy and all too common to deny that a problem exists.

Listen to yourself

How you are thinking and speaking – get in touch with why you feel the way you do. Are your expectations of self realistic, or are others expecting more than you can or know how to give?

Why am I doing this job?

Do you still feel motivated to make a difference to the lives of people you work with and care for? The people you care for and work with may not be able to convey to you fully how valuable is the relationship you have with them . It is okay to ask yourself real questions.

What would help?

Ask yourself what would make things better or easier for you to manage how you are feeling and the circumstances you find yourself in. Is the answer within your control or do you need support?

Support: where do you find it?

Do you have a mentor, buddy, trusted friend/colleague who you can talk to at work, whom you are willing to take guidance and counsel from? We all need such a person. If not at work, explore other options.

Be who you are

Give yourself permission to be yourself. Bring the whole person to work – your skills; abilities and passions. It really is important also to have other interests outside of the work place. They help you to be more effective in other areas of your life and help when work feels all consuming.

Working together

Think about 'TEAM': '**T**ogether **E**veryone **A**chieves **M**ore'. Choose your attitude, even when others do not. What works for the people you work with and care for also works for you. This is about us not them. It is about relationships. It is about team. Ask: How can we be the best we can be together?

"I've learned that people will forget what you said, people will forget what you did, but people will never forget how you made them feel."

— *MAYA ANGELOU*

Share the burden

There are many competing priorities on your time. Use staff breaks and meetings to share and talk about the difficult stuff and not just tasks that need completing. Think about how circumstances make you really feel and share this so you develop and learn how to handle those feelings well together.

Value your experience

Remember it is good to talk and not bottle up how you feel. You can be a force for change for the better. Your experience both in the tough times and in the good times can be used to create a culture of shared values and support.

Know you matter

Remind yourself that you are a real person, making real decisions which really affect other people as well as yourself.

9

Valuing and working with residents/family/friends

Treating residents with dignity, respect and without discrimination – easy to say, vital to do

JEREMY NIXEY

After four years teaching, Jeremy established Shaw which created ten Welsh Housing Associations then set up Shaw healthcare and its 75 care homes.

A carer provides intimate and personal support: a position of privilege and power. How you use this power will earn the love and respect of those you care for or their bitter resentment. Respect them and they will love you for what you do; disrespect them and you will be resented and make those you 'care' for angry. Being a good carer is both simple and very hard; you must treat those you care for as you would yourself like to be treated. Easy? Not many of us in any walk of life manage it very well.

Know those you care for

Get to know all you can about those you care for: what they are most proud of and the key people in their lives

What is the person for whom you are caring thinking of?

Talk to their relatives and friends and find out all you can about their lives. Relate – don't challenge or confront. If someone is eagerly expecting their long dead partner to walk through the door, share in their anticipation and lead their happy thoughts on to something in the present.

Don't intrude uninvited into their personal space

Don't presume their consent to anything you have to do to or for them. Turn essential care actions – taking tablets, weighing or taking someone to the toilet – into projects you and they work on together.

Sensitive control

Sometimes you have to be the controlling one in this relationship: Tablets and toilets are needed even when not wanted. The parent in you needs to persuade and win consent – somehow.

With love, or careless coercion?

For one receiving your care the feel of your hands and the tone of your voice can be the language of love. But uncaring hands, unprepared actions, done to someone without their consent, are coercive actions and, as with any of us, provoke an aggressive response. The anger may not be evident but concealed and show only as sullenness or depression.

Engage fully

Keep eye contact all the time and always engage the person in what you are planning to do; don't chat to others while caring for them – and especially don't talk across them to others while you are helping them with any action.

Try to bridge the communication gap

Frustration and anger are the natural feelings of someone whose dementia hinders their ability to communicate fully their thoughts and feelings to you – understand this and try and bridge the gap.

Horses for courses...

Build affectionate but appropriate relationships with everyone you care for; "Good evening Mr Smith: how has your day gone so far?" will be right for one, just as "John you old bugger; what trouble have you been causing today?" is right for another. Don't get them the wrong way round!

Anecdote

A carer heard Bill say "I would love to see the sea once more". So she came in on her day off, took him to the sea in her car and then sat beside him for a long time while he soaked in the experience, and then drove him home. Two days later he died.

... but no favourites!

You belong to all those you care for – don't have favourites or you will exclude and discriminate against others. If you are good at your job (and if you love those you care for you will become very good at your job) your friendship and respect will be important to every person in the home or house. Remember they all have an equal claim on your time and affection – be sure they all get a fair share of you and that you don't spend most time only with the charming ones.

Do unto others...

If you always treat everyone you care for as you would yourself wish to be treated then you will always give the finest personal care, with total dignity at all times and you will never discriminate against anyone.

Involving residents and relatives in care home management

PAULINE SHAW
is director of care & service development with The Royal Star & Garter Homes, a Charity for ex-Service men and women.

To truly involve residents and relatives relies upon a culture which encourages them to directly influence the management of their care home. Care leaders need the courage to actively seek resident feedback, knowing that the response may challenge their perceptions. Words must be translated into actions and if this is not feasible, the reasons explained. Ultimately, there are no ifs, buts or maybes – no excuses. We must involve the people who choose to live with us, not for a regulatory tick box, but because it is quite simply, the right thing to do.

Commit to a person-centred approach

Adopt the philosophy that people who choose to live in your care homes have an absolute right to be involved in the way in which 'their' home is managed. Create life stories for residents by asking what is important to them in their day-to-day lives, as well as understanding past memories and influences.

Have a strategic plan for involvement

It is time well spent developing a plan, highlighting effective methods for consultation and involvement, including staff who know the residents best. Be committed to exploring new ideas which involve residents or are influenced by them.

Provide regular resident meetings

Hold monthly meetings for residents and staff to share information and give feedback. The quality of day-to-day experiences of residents is how we should measure our success, and their influence shines a spotlight on whether you are getting it right.

Commission an independent annual satisfaction survey

An annual survey, preferably undertaken independently, provides valuable opportunities for resident and relative involvement. It is helpful to design a questionnaire which covers core areas such as quality of nursing/care, catering, activities and communication. The feedback is then reviewed and improvements and changes made as a result.

Invite relatives to a regular afternoon tea

There is benefit from an informal approach, and what better way than inviting relatives to join you and some staff to tea? The first session could set the scene and ask what residents would like to learn more about; stimulate lively interaction rather than allow it to become a complaints sessions.

Promote people's individuality

Providers who are passionate about supporting individuality and identity will invite people to furnish and personalise their room with items of importance. To have familiar items around them, personal to them, significant to them will enhance wellbeing and happiness.

Customer care equals quality care

We must commit to continually improve the quality of care by not just listening but by acting upon feedback from residents and relatives, e.g. complaints, meetings and audit/surveys. The benefits include greater resident satisfaction, enhanced relationships with relatives and increased staff morale and confidence.

Involve residents in recruitment of key staff

Resident involvement in recruitment, e.g. for an activities co-ordinator, provides first hand insight. Each candidate is given a brief to facilitate a suitable 20 minute activities session for a group of five residents. Residents' views are later gathered on the candidate's approach, attitude, and whether the residents enjoyed the session. We aim to involve residents in selecting other staff as we know others have done this with success.

"When you really listen to another person from their point of view, and reflect back to them that understanding, it's like giving them emotional oxygen."

– STEPHEN COVEY

Making environmental changes inclusive

When considering making changes to residents' environments, such as a room redecoration programme, provide residents with a choice of decor (e.g. shades from a colour spectrum) for real empowerment and influence on the environment in which they live.

Before purchasing new equipment - involve the end user

Before introducing new equipment for residents, ask if they will participate in trialling the item first. For example, new beds, mattresses, cutlery or crockery. Not everybody's expectations will be met, but this process promotes involvement and better communicates the reasoning behind the final decision.

Communicating with residents

DR JENNIE POWELL

has been a speech & language therapist with Cardiff Memory Team for 20 years. Jennie is author of 'Care to Communicate' published by Hawker. She is now a carer for a parent with dementia.

How do we think and communicate? A thought or idea is made up of images in the mind – internal pictures, smells, sounds, tastes and feelings. We communicate these ideas with others using words, facial expressions and body language. Many residents have difficulty with images and words. This can cause fear, frustration and distress. Skilled carers can help compensate for this communication breakdown, making a vital difference to quality of life.

Keep sensory channels open

What we see and hear affects our mind images and thinking. If glasses are smeary or a hearing aid is not working, residents will struggle to make sense of the world. Images will be muddled and confusion will arise. Help clean their glasses every day and know how to check that a hearing aid is working.

Remind them what is happening

It can be frightening if images of who you are, where you are, your past and present do not come to mind. This is the daily reality for many residents. Help by reminding them where they are and what's happening. Keep doing this as memory may be short. A written note summarising key facts may be useful.

Be with them and reassure

Being alone with unclear mind images can be distressing. Panic and anxiety may set in. Just being with them, sitting with them, even in silence or while you are engaged in a task of your own, can be reassuring. Perhaps remind them that "everything's fine".

Be positive

Our mood is determined by images that form in our mind about our daily concerns, tasks and activities. If a resident has difficulty with mind images, they may take their cue from you. If you are positive and relaxed, they too are likely to feel this way.

Know who they really are

A seemingly illogical behaviour may be a remnant from a resident's past, a well-learned habit or past routine that fills their mind when new images don't form. The person who repeatedly smoothes the table may have been a cleaner, the person who keeps moving the furniture may once have done this for a living. Knowing the person's true history is vital.

Avoid confrontation

Where a reaction seems illogical, try to avoid confrontation and do not challenge. Perhaps distract and move the person on to another topic or task. If they are very anxious or upset and can't move on, perhaps try clarifying their feelings for them with a response such as "I'm sorry you're upset". This can help the person feel understood and can dissipate a stressful situation.

Gently guide them through their day

When images do not form easily, the person may feel lost and unsure what they should do. Rather than dictate, gently make suggestions "Maybe you'd like to brush your hair?" It is important to feel in control of our own life.

"An abnormal reaction to an abnormal situation is normal behaviour."
— VIKTOR E. FRANKL, MAN'S SEARCH FOR MEANING

Offer appropriate environment and stimulation

Surroundings can reassure or confuse. A view outside, a newspaper, an old photograph or object from the past may be reassuring or a source of anxiety. Does taking part in an activity give pleasure or would they prefer to sit back and watch. Learn what helps and what stresses each individual.

Take time to explain, to listen and understand

You may need to simplify your words and shorten your sentences. Reword and repeat if they do not understand. If their words fail, look for the underlying meaning – learn to interpret their emotions, facial expressions and body language.

Kindness costs nothing

How would you like to be treated?

Working with family and friends

JUDY DOWNEY

studied at the London School of Economics, worked in social care and social and political research. She then moved to the Department of Health and is now chair of the Relatives & Residents Association.

Care home entry equals failure in too many minds. But a care home can be the best possible solution for lots of older people. It can mean a new start and a fresh lease of life. A good diet, caring staff and individual, thoughtful care in a friendly, stimulating environment can be the best choice. Losing your home can be a terrible wrench, equally traumatic for those closest to the resident. But there are many ways for relatives and friends to keep in contact and play an important part in supporting the person they care about in their new home.

Feeling welcome

Welcoming visitors and making them feel at home can make all the difference. Family and friends also need to be involved in the creation, updating and review of the care plan. This means gathering information about the resident's past, family, work and health history, tastes, hobbies and preferences.

The past is the key to the present

For many, the past is all that remains and family and friends can help staff to unlock, recapture and rekindle past times and past joys and bring them alive again. It is important to remember that the people and places left behind are still crucial, even when the resident may have little awareness of their role and relationship.

Managers matter

Managers, as always, lay the foundations and set the tone. Care staff will take the lead from them and if they consider friends and families as active partners who care and want to be included, wherever they live, life will be easier and better all round.

The contract

It is important for families and friends to know what is – and isn't – included in the contract at the outset, as well as whether there are visits they need to organise or items which they may be able to provide.

Knowing their rights

Those who are nearest and dearest to the resident need to be involved and included in their life and the life of the home. They need to know that both they and the resident have rights, enshrined in law. Knowing that there are regulations and standards and that an inspectorate exists to protect residents can give them confidence to become involved.

Forums help participation

Forums for relatives and residents work well but need encouragement and support from the home. They can be useful in building relationships, raising concerns, making positive suggestions and getting more involved.

Good communication makes for better care

Care staff who communicate what's going on and keep in touch really matter. Relatives generally want to know that their mum or partner had a head cold or is not eating well or is sleeping badly. They may know what works best for them, if they know there's a problem.

"Nurses and care workers have two contracts: one with their employer which is written, and one with their patient which is unwritten. When conflict arises between the two it is the unwritten contract which should be observed."

– FOREWORD TO *"SANS EVERYTHING"* BY RUSSELL BARTON, CONSULTANT PSYCHIATRIST, 1967

Support during health visits

Family and friends usually want to know from the staff if there are any medical/dental/optical appointments pending. They can be helpful in providing a reassuring presence or if they know about changes in medication or treatment.

Listen and respond to complaints

It matters to listen and note concerns and complaints as well as compliments and, of course, to respond and learn from them. When things go wrong, it is often as hard for those raising them as for care staff to hear them. When questions are asked, it's always better to find someone with the answer than to stonewall and be defensive.

Open and sincere relationships

Relatives and friends want good open relationships with the home and the staff. There aren't many perfect places anywhere and tastes and expectations differ. Most people don't want to be seen as difficult or demanding, so it's important to remember who they are and why they care. We'd want them to do it for us, after all.

10
Activities

Supporting the workforce to engage with residents through activity

JACKIE POOL

is chief executive of Jackie Pool Associates Ltd, and developer of the Pool Activity Level (PAL) instrument for occupational profiling – supporting an activity model of care.

The role of managers and senior care workers in supporting the wellbeing of people who use their service relies on an understanding and commitment to enable participation in a full range of activity. Having a sense of agency, being able to do what one is capable of, is a human need that drives behaviour and that should be fulfilled through enabling approaches by skilled care givers and activity providers. When the workforce is supported to meet this need in those who use their services, wellbeing will be experienced not only by residents but also by staff.

Personal care is an activity

An activity model of care views everything a person does as having the potential to be a fulfilling activity. This means that personal care should be an activity and not a task, with care workers understanding what an individual can do and how they like to do it.

Care workers' role

Care workers should be encouraged to value their role in activity engagement where personal care is an opportunity for activity too. They should never describe their role as being inferior to that of activity providers or use negative language such as 'just' being a care worker. Managers and supervisors can support this positive view of the role of all team members.

The right level of activity

The right level of activity is achieved by understanding what each activity demands of the individual and what are the abilities and limitations of the individual. This includes identifying the physical, cognitive and social skills of the person for each activity and analysing how the activity can be presented to use these skills.

Not only 'what' but 'how'

Care plans should explain not only what activities care workers should be supporting an individual with, but also how to support them. Each activity should be recorded to identify what the individual can manage on their own and how this can be achieved. It also needs to identify where the individual needs support and how this should be given.

Recognise care workers' achievements

Care workers should be supported to value their role in engaging the individual in meaningful activity, through effective supervision and the reinforcement of good care practice by managers and supervisors. The reporting of positive events in handovers about the achievements of individuals is one way of doing this.

Positive language

Terms such as "supporting the person to get dressed, dine, use the toilet" reinforces positive care activity practice. Negative language ("toileting them, feeding them, dressing them") reveals a non-person-centred, task oriented approach.

Relationship-centred approach

Care workers should be seen engaging with individuals while supporting them to carry out person-centred care activities. This relationship-centred approach recognises the feelings of the individual and responds accordingly, using sensitive and validating communication skills.

Working together

Activity providers and care workers should be encouraged to work together to share their knowledge and understanding of the individuals that they are supporting.

Case History

The manager of a care setting described her activity team as good but the care team is having problems. We brought the teams together as one, with some members having leisure activity skills and others having care activity skills. Now the team is working together and residents are active and engaged.

Spontaneous activity

Leisure activities are not the sole province of an activity provider – a few minutes of spontaneous activity from any member of the team can make a world of difference. Managers and senior care workers who reinforce the benefits of this when they see anyone carrying out a spontaneous activity will encourage it to happen more.

Personal activity programmes

In addition to group activity programmes, each person should have their own individual activity programme highlighting regular activities that are part of the individual's routine and habits. These can be a combination of personal care, domestic and leisure activities, including hobbies and interests. The programme should identify the timing of the activities and where they take place as well as anything that is important to the individual for the successful completion of the activity.

Brilliant practical activities in care homes

LYNDA LEEN

was the first activity organiser to be appointed by Colten Care 24 years ago. She is involved in the local community and church.

Activities in the care industry are essential for both mental and physical stimulation. Motivating residents is the vital point, working alongside your manager and staff team to achieve this. Outlined below are 10 useful pointers when planning activities but remember, most of all, you are there for the residents. Ensuring they are comfortable is the key, no matter what activity is being put on. An inviting room with good lighting, heating and ventilation is a must. Always ask if residents are comfortable. Make sure you speak clearly, do not shout and remember that smiley face.

Horses for courses

Would you yourself want to participate in the activities that are offered in your home? Is there variety to suit all capabilities? Are men and women catered for? Is the activity practical to suit the building or environment? Make sure you offer activities that stimulate mentally as well as physically.

Never too old

Do not assume that the residents are too old. They often say "we are never too old to learn". Encourage new skills and rekindle old ones.

Evening engagements

Sometimes, offering an early evening activity (to start after the evening meal around 6.45pm, especially in the winter with the darker evenings), is very popular. This is an opportunity to have a speaker or presentation. Another option would be a musical entertainer followed by light refreshments.

A listening ear

Don't be shocked by what a resident has to say, consider it flattering that they can be so open with you. Remember that a lot of the residents have been through a war, have been married and brought up a family. Now the residential building is their home where they can offload a lot of their problems. We sometimes cannot give them the answers that they want to have but we can be sympathetic to their needs.

Have a 'Plan B'

Be prepared to be spontaneous. For example, if an outside entertainer cannot attend, have another activity ready e.g. a quiz. If the weather is fine take the activity outside and ask the chef if lunch could go alfresco. We have lots of cold, wet days so make the most of the fine weather when it occurs.

In and about the garden

Be practical, often the simplest activity can be inspiring. A talk on gardening can bring back residents' memories of their own gardens and stimulate discussion on how well the home's garden is doing. This can lead onto a discussion on famous gardens residents have visited either in this country or abroad.

What's to celebrate?

Do not assume residents want to celebrate certain occasions such as Valentine's Day. This might not be a happy reminder for certain residents who may have lost loved ones. Always be sensitive to residents' needs.

Consult and plan

Have regular staff meetings where activities are on the agenda, and have regular activity meetings too with the residents so they can give their opinions on what activities they would like, if there is something they did not enjoy or have a burning ambition they would like to take up. Again be practical and never promise to do something you cannot fulfill.

Case History

A dream came true for one resident. Having to leave her home, a farm, and the horses was like bereavement for her. Using my pony and trap I was able to let her groom my pony and ride in the trap, making her feel young again.

All working together

Fund-raising can be a chance for residents, staff, relatives and friends to work together. Remember residents may have experience in this field, use their ideas and suggestions. Praise staff for their teamwork and help with fundraising activities.

Engage with the wider community

Get involved with your local community. Many residents will have been members of different organisations such as the University of the Third Age, Lions, Masons, Rotary, Community Centres and church groups as well as charities like RNLI, RSPB or Barnardo's. Where possible, encourage residents to get involved with these groups, or invite the groups to have meetings in the home. Invite guest speakers to the home or ask residents to talk about their own experiences within groups.

A creative approach to activities

SARAH ZOUTEWELLE-MORRIS

is an artist and the author of the runaway best seller,

'Chocolate Rain, 100 ideas for a creative approach to activities in dementia care'.

Hello, I'm Lilian, a 76-year-old artist, designer, and dancer. For medical reasons I now live in a care institution. Please don't call it a 'home' – for me it isn't. I've left my beautiful house and garden, my neighbours, and the gentle rhythm of my days – in short, everything which gave me a sense of comfort, usefulness, and connection. How will I find meaning for my days here? Next to simple human kindness, a creative attitude is most helpful. May I share some of my thoughts from a lifetime in the arts? I know you are more creative than you might think.

Quick start guide to a creative approach

The following principles operate across all artistic disciplines: Pay attention; cultivate an open attitude; take risks; learn tolerance for uncertainty; relinquish the need to always be in control; focus on the process not the outcome; experiment; laugh, and play!

Meet me as an equal

Please, risk stepping out of your professional role of helper and simply be with me. You might feel uneasy, but your willingness to also be a little vulnerable will enable me to give to you, and it will make me feel less helpless.

Use your imagination to look beyond my condition

My long productive life is not apparent when you see me. I've had a stroke and my speech is impaired, but my intelligence is absolutely intact. To see me as I was at the height of my dancing career, you will need imagination – please use it.

Give your full attention

Watch anyone engaged creatively and see how concentrated they are. Undivided attention is one of the most precious gifts we can give and receive from others. It is in itself, a healing act.

Don't worry so much about the outcome

In any creative activity, the journey is often more important than the destination. Trusting the process to lead somewhere, even if you aren't sure where that may be, ensures enjoyment and success regardless of the end result.

No children's activities, please

I was recently obliged to attend a resident's birthday celebration. I don't like group activities, and the party was better suited to 5-year-olds. Please use your creativity to find things which fit with my interests and background.

Meaning and connection, not busyness

Ironically, I've been removed from my busy life and plonked here where there's nothing to do. Then you folks have to break your brains to keep me occupied! Please, forget about that – instead be creative: if you bathe me or bring me my meal with your full attention you will find many ways to improvise and make it meaningful for both of us. That way everything becomes an 'activity'.

Open attitude

Anyone already 'knowing' what I can and can't do is a real killer to creativity, which is about 'finding out'. Bring attention and curiosity to our encounter and we both may end up learning something.

Be willing to look foolish

As an artist, when following an idea, I know there will be a point where I don't know what to do next. This is a crucial moment in every creative process! You may need to risk doing something different. And don't worry about making mistakes, they can lead to something new and they'll make us laugh!

Smile, fresh air is good for your teeth!

Laughter works more wonders than all the drugs in the pharmacy. I love humour, and sharing a giggle will bring us closer and lighten both our days. Thank you, dear, for listening.

"Many of the cranky old are like mythical creatures, if you hang on tightly enough and don't let them throw you then they calm down and even give you something, a gift, a blessing. Of course there were some who simply threw things."

– Jonathan Rosen

Reflections on activities in homes after many years running NAPA

SYLVIE SILVER

is director of the National Activity Providers Association (NAPA) and is passionate about wellbeing and quality of life for older people in care settings supported by trained staff.

NAPA aims to support care staff to enable older people to live life the way they choose with meaning and purpose. This vision of activity provision is shared by more and more managers. The challenge for many is how to achieve this goal amid all the other 'needs' that have to be met. I have tried to capture here the key areas for change that might have real impact on how activity provision looks in your care home. Addressing just one of them could make a difference. Tackling all ten would bring about a culture change, as many managers have successfully done.

Large groups are fast becoming a thing of the past
A person-centred approach leads to groups of 4 - 6 like-minded residents coming together for short sessions. Activity staff are often praised for getting large numbers together. Ask yourself, why is that a good thing?

What is that resident doing and why?
This is a key question to ask every time you move about the home. If residents are sat in a lounge with no apparent purpose, other than to be kept an eye on, then perhaps sitting somewhere else might be a nicer experience.

Listen to your residents
Each resident is an individual and will have different needs. It is often the little things, that make a big difference, that get ignored. A chance to sit in the garden every day would be bliss for some and boredom for others but do all your staff really know who enjoys what?

Bring life stories to life!
Gathering life stories is the only way to ensure you know how someone would usually like to spend their day and what holds meaning for them. Sadly life story details often get trapped in care plans kept under lock and key.

Support and direction
Activity co-ordinators are often isolated in their role and need support and direction from managers in order to do a good job. Do you have a clear idea of what you want to see happening and do the activity team understand what you want?

Activity is everyone's job

Does your induction training include your vision of activities? Making time for new staff members to shadow the activity staff can make a difference to understanding why activity is important and the part they can play.

Examine work practices

Meeting social care needs has to have just as much time and attention paid to it as meeting physical needs. Many carers claim they have no time to support activities. Looking critically at working practices, and how care time is spent, has proved to be a positive exercise in increasing meaningful engagement for some managers.

"The days are very long when the walls are the same."

– A CARE HOME RESIDENT LIVING WITH DEMENTIA

Limit the use of TVs

Look in your lounges and see who is really watching television properly? We are taught from an early age not to talk when the TV is on – how many residents are chatting and how many have their eyes closed? Do the carers believe the residents are engaged because the television is on?

Mealtimes should be the most sociable part of the day

Does your dining room 'hum' like a restaurant full of happy customers ? Make sure medication is not given during a meal. Encourage staff to sit down and chat at the tables rather than hover around. Make sure you eat with residents sometimes so that you share their experience.

Banish the tea trolley!

Tea trolleys are the last surviving symbol of an institution. Making tea has been part of life for many. Helping to make your own tea means making it the way you like it. Serving afternoon tea around a big communal table can meet many needs at once and encourages conversation.

11
Special challenges

Meeting the challenge of behaviours that challenge

PROF. GRAHAM STOKES

is director of dementia care at Bupa Care Services and honorary visiting professor of person-centred dementia care, University of Bradford.

What are behaviours that challenge? This is not complicated – they are behaviours that carers, whether they be family or professional, cannot cope with, because if they could cope they would not be challenged. And the behaviours that carers struggle to cope with tend to be those that are called "acts of commission" (e.g. shouting, agitation, aggressive outbursts, walking with risk, inappropriate toileting conduct, repetitive questioning), rather than "acts of omission" (i.e. dependency). As families often say, "I can cope with what (s)he can no longer do, but I can't cope with what s(he) has started to do".

The impact of behaviours that challenge

Behaviours that challenge cause distress to people with dementia who are experiencing them, have a negative impact on the wellbeing of others and are associated with reduced quality of life for all.

Symptoms or not?

With the exception of frontal dementias and dementia with Lewy bodies, behaviours that challenge are not symptoms of dementia.

Meaningless or meaningful?

Instead of being understood as symptoms to be controlled, behaviours that challenge are either reactions to unsupportive care settings or the expression of a person's unmet needs, some of which will be unknown for they will be buried deep within who the person is. Hence behaviours that challenge are not random, meaningless acts but are often meaningful actions to be understood.

How do we know?

Or, the question that enabled the paradigm shift from pathology to person – "Why are only some people with dementia challenging?" All people with dementia have problems with memory, communication and thinking, and hence all become dependent, but not all people with dementia are challenging.

An adage to hold on to

The guiding principle when understanding behaviour in dementia is "That which people with dementia share in common you can attribute to the disease, that which they do not share in common you can rarely attribute to the disease."

People and places

Those people who are challenging in their behaviours can be context-bound. If a person is rarely challenging in the company of certain people, or in a certain place, this clearly says more about the person and the place they find themselves in and less about the disease for if their behaviours were in fact symptoms, such inconsistency could never happen for their dementia is constant and enduring.

The role of antipsychotics

If behaviours that challenge present with unacceptable risk, or the person is extremely distressed, then prescribing antipsychotic medication is recommended but in all instances, the need to identify effective alternative therapeutic approaches is pressing, if for no other reason than antipsychotics for most people with dementia are ineffective and have the potential to cause stroke and premature death.

"Discovery consists of seeing what everybody has seen and thinking what nobody has thought."

– ALBERT SZENT-GYORGI

Look for the causes

As behaviours that challenge are often the result of unmet need, be a detective and decipher a person's actions for these are the building bricks to understand who the person is and what they need.

Quality of care

Behaviours that challenge can be reactions to actions of others. To minimise the likelihood of challenging reactions, personal space should be respected, approaches should be paced, people should be listened to and communication should not be rushed. Requests couched in terms of 'must', 'have to', or 'should' are to be avoided for these increase the risk of confrontation. Before imposing on a person with dementia a 'have to', ask yourself, if the person doesn't want to do it, does it really matter?

Quality of life

Care settings ought to provide a sense of familiarity and belonging; low-arousal environments are calming and soothing; and we need to ask ourselves what quality of life are people being offered? Are people meaningfully occupied, for what is the point of getting a person ready for the day if their day never begins!

Working with sexuality issues

Prof. Graham Jackson

is Alzheimer Scotland Professor of Dementia Care, University West of Scotland. Prior to this he was a consultant old age psychiatrist in Glasgow.

Dr Elizabeth Lightbody

graduated from University of Edinburgh Medical School in 2004. She has worked in psychiatry since 2006 and Is currently a higher specialist trainee in old age psychiatry in the West of Scotland.

Care home staff often feel uncomfortable when residents exhibit sexual behaviour. This can take many forms, for example intimate relationships with other residents, masturbating in public or touching carers inappropriately. Just because someone lives in a care home does not mean they lose their right to have a sexual identity. Activity which appears sexual may represent a need for intimacy or for basic human contact, which may otherwise be absent. Such behaviour is usually more uncomfortable for professionals and family carers than for the person with dementia.

Right to express sexuality

Having a diagnosis of dementia, and being in a care home, does not change the basic human right to express sexuality. However we must also consider the impact of sexual behaviour on others, as with any behaviour in a communal setting.

A sexual history on admission?

On admission, a sexual history is as important and as helpful as taking note of their likes and dislikes around food, how they like to dress, their sleeping habits, etc.

Capacity

If someone with dementia becomes involved in a sexual relationship, do they have the capacity to consent? In law, sex without consent is rape but where cognition is impaired, what level of understanding is required for consent? Is it enough to use previous behaviour to judge what someone would want now? We must think about these issues carefully in every situation, and discuss with everyone involved, including family members.

Misidentification

The presence of dementia can lead to a resident misidentifying another resident as their partner and so try to be intimate with them. This upsetting attachment can occur even when their spouse is visiting regularly and obviously needs to be handled sensitively.

Privacy

In communal settings it is sometimes difficult to create privacy for couples who may previously have enjoyed regular intimacy. Staff should think about making private space available, for example using "do not disturb" signs.

Sharing information about incidents

When an incident occurs it is important to keep everyone involved informed. Discussions with relatives may be very delicate and should always involve an experienced manager who knows them well. Homes must have a pre-existing policy on when to inform agencies such as social services or even the police.

Staff attitudes

Everyone has their own views on what behaviour is considered acceptable. A manager must ensure consistency and respect in their care settings. Although a resident or staff member may be very distressed by a resident masturbating in public, the appropriate response should be to ensure that this can happen in private, rather than trying to stop it.

"Lost love is still love, it takes a different form, that's all. You can't see their smile or bring them food or tousle their hair or move them around a dance floor. But when those senses weaken, another heightens. Memory. Memory becomes your partner. You nurture it."

– MITCH ALBOM, *THE FIVE PEOPLE YOU MEET IN HEAVEN*

Drug treatment

Drug treatment should always be a last resort. There is no convincing evidence drugs (antipsychotics, anti-androgens, antidepressants and anxiolytics) benefit those showing challenging sexual behaviour.

Avoid labeling people

In all walks of life we label people, but we should try to avoid such labeling as it changes how the facts are perceived. For example someone with dementia exposing himself may be labeled "a dirty old man" which is likely to influence inappropriately how, and indeed where, he is cared for.

Be prepared to work with risk

Any course of action when working with people exhibiting challenging sexual behaviour is likely to have risks, and have both a positive and negative impact. Care home staff should be able to identify these and consider how likely and how severe they might be when making decisions.

Taking a modern approach to restraint

PROF. RHIDIAN HUGHES
is Visiting Professor in social care at Buckinghamshire New University and Visiting Academic in gerontology at King's College London.

For many years there has been concern about the use of restraint on people who use social care services. The term restraint covers a wide range of activities by means of which an individual's freedom of movement is restricted, and when limits are placed on a person's will or ability. Following high profile cases of abuse, such as at Winterbourne View, a focus on reducing restraint has never been more important.

Restraint in care settings takes many forms

Some actions can be clearly identified as restraint, for example physical interventions which restrict movement. Other activities are subtler and may be less easy to recognise as potential forms of restraint such as the threat of force or the use of electronic surveillance devices.

When required (prn) prescribing of tranquillisers is highly questionable

Covert medication involves the use of drugs to make people drowsy, docile and compliant (through drugs collectively known as tranquillisers). When required (prn) prescribing leaves the administration of these drugs open to abuse.

Remember the laws of the land

The inappropriate use of restraint can be against criminal and civil law. False imprisonment, common assault and malicious wounding are illegal. 'Distraction techniques', which inflict pain to encourage people to comply or as a consequence of doing something, are corporal punishment.

Restraint can be justified in some situations

There are circumstances when the use of restraint is justifiable to prevent harm to individuals themselves or to those around them. Chemical restraint may be helpful, for example, when someone is distressed and undergoing an invasive procedure such as catheterisation. In this case sedation may help to ensure the procedure is carried out quickly and effectively.

Any restraint must serve the best interests of people using services, not the staff

The restriction of someone's movement, regardless of whether they resist or the extent of their mental capacity, should uphold the principles of 'best interests'. The amount and type of restraint should be proportionate to the likelihood and seriousness of the harm needing to be prevented. Restraint used for staff convenience is never justifiable.

The circumstances that lead up to restraint need to be identified and understood

Staff may face challenging and violent behaviour from people in their care. However, it is important to see individuals' behaviour as forms of communications, largely arising from their needs, rather than as people with 'problems' to be managed. Restraint does nothing to address the underlying causes of challenging behaviour and a focus on person-centred care will get to the root cause of any challenging or violent behaviour.

Restraint compromises care outcomes

The experience of being restrained can be harrowing for those involved and can lead to anxiety and confusion. This in turn may prompt challenging behaviour. The over-prescribing of anti-psychotic drugs can lead to clinical complications including slowing rehabilitation, falls and injuries and cognitive decline for people with dementia.

"Force is all-conquering, but its victories are short lived."

– ABRAHAM LINCOLN

Organisational structures and cultures all play a part

Restraint is more common in group settings. Organisations are better equipped to minimise or eliminate restraint when they: listen and engage with people using their services and empower them in making choices about their care. Also important is a person-centred care and organisational culture; using data to track any restraint to learn from it; investing in staff through training; and having strong leaders that focus on people.

Keep learning

Awareness and knowledge about restraint – from the causes to the consequences – is essential when staff are supporting potentially vulnerable people using care services. There are lots of resources to support learning. For example online resources include http://tinyurl.com/restraintresource1 and there are books exploring a range of perspectives http://tinyurl.com/restraintresource2 http://tinyurl.com/restraintresource3

If there is one thing to remember about restraint, it is this:

Any form of restraint should only be adopted in the most extreme cases and once all other options have been exhausted. Restraint can easily tip over into abuse.

Making sure your residents with dementia eat well

IAN WEATHERHEAD

has been in nursing since the 1970s and is currently lead nurse of Admiral Nursing DIRECT, a national helpline for those affected by dementia.

Appropriate nutrition and hydration is essential for our wellbeing. However, care staff are faced with many considerations when caring for someone in late stage dementia whose nutritional needs and intake are likely to change significantly as end of life approaches. The following are areas for consideration for all when caring for someone with dementia.

Focus

Concentrate on me when helping me eat, do not have conversations with other colleagues. Talk to me even though I may not be able to respond. Tell me what's happening in the world even if I can't talk back.

Swallowing

Before putting that next spoon or fork of food in my mouth, have I have swallowed the last mouthful? Did you see me swallow? Watch my throat when eating, if I still have food in my mouth show me how to swallow, I may have forgotten.

Food preparation

If I am on a soft diet that doesn't mean everything has to be liquidised! Be creative with foods. If I cannot tell you what some of my favourite foods are, ask my family. For instance, I may love scrambled egg, and ice cream, but not together. I don't like grey slop.

Meal times

I may not be hungry at designated meal times, I may have worked odd hours in my life and eaten at different times. I would like to eat if and when I am hungry. Remember, you are here to meet my needs, not the other way round.

Artificial hydration

No tubes please. Tube feeding will not cure me or improve my quality of life. If I am at the end stage of life I would prefer to be kept comfortable and have a peaceful death, not a briefly prolonged life to meet someone else's needs.

Weight

Losing weight is normal in end stage of dementia. Please also inform my family of this, if they know this is to be expected it might be less distressing for them, *but* . . . that's not an excuse not to offer me food if I can still eat!

Utensils

If I can still feed myself, make sure the crockery is plain coloured so I can see food easily on it. Make sure I can still hold cutlery. I may need prompting to eat in case I have forgotten. If I wear glasses, are they are clean, and are they mine?

Oral hygiene

If I'm not eating, check my mouth. Are my gums sore, are there any ulcers? If I still have my own teeth, please help me ensure they are clean. If I have dentures then make sure they are mine . . . sharing has its limits. If I'm dying please keep my mouth clean and comfortable.

"We seem to have forgotten the difference between the people who die because they have stopped taking in food and water, and people who stop taking in food and water because of the natural dying process."

– Scott, L. D., Kutac, J. E., & McCammon, S. D. (2011). Artificial nutrition and hydration: the evolution of ethics, evidence, and policy. Journal of General Internal Medicine, 26(9), 1053-1058).

Liquids

A sip of liquid may help me swallow, but don't choke me with food and drink together. If I'm not hungry keep offering me drinks. Dehydration commonly causes more problems than missing a meal.

See me

Sit with me when eating, don't stand over me. Make eye contact, smile, and engage with me. Make me feel my life is still important, not just another chore to be dealt with. I was you once, and one day you may be me.

Supporting residents with mental health issues

DR AMANDA THOMPSELL

is a consultant old age psychiatrist. She has a long term special interest in mental health issues in care homes.

Mental health issues are difficult at the best of times. When the person is elderly, has physical needs and feels dislocated at being placed in an unfamiliar care home setting, then this is not the best of times. With care home staff not always being trained to deal with mental health issues, and medical services not always being focused on the care home sector, it is no wonder that mental health issues regularly go undiagnosed and untreated. Often, all that is needed is proper recognition of the problem, and good communication and co-ordination between professionals. The following suggestions might help:

Confirm ongoing provision

For any new resident, especially younger ones or residents from out of your normal catchment, always confirm who will provide ongoing mental health input. This avoids debate and delay when support is needed.

Prompt recognition of early symptoms

When you are dealing with someone's mental health needs, check, and ask about that person's symptoms so you are prepared should they relapse. Everyone has unique symptoms that recur when their mental health deteriorates. Knowing what to watch for could mean a relapse is recognised and treated more quickly and effectively.

Time spent listening at admission is well-spent

Transition to a care home is a time of great stress for the resident – and the resident's family and friends. Extra time in ensuring a smooth transition and in listening to the family's concerns and emotions (often loss, sorrow, anger, guilt) will have a huge impact on longer term relationships.

Have a list of medications available

If a resident is due to see mental health services make sure you have the life history and details of the resident's physical health ready and available. Some psychiatric drugs can be contraindicated if the person has particular medical conditions and a list of current medication being taken is also essential to avoid potential adverse drug reactions.

Be aware of possible depression

Remember your resident may be depressed. Depression is often missed as no one thinks about it. Staff should understand that residents can have (and many do have) depression as well as dementia.

Report changes to the mental health team

Information needed if the mental health team is seeing your resident for depression includes any changes in appetite or weight; changes in sleep pattern especially early morning wakening; any change in mood particularly in the morning and any change in the amount of engagement with activities or if they becoming socially withdrawn. Make sure you have this information ready.

Take negative expressions seriously

If a resident says "I don't feel life is worth living" or "I wish I was dead" take this seriously and bring it to the attention of senior staff and the medical team. An assessment of the risk of suicide is probably needed. Any attempt at self-harm (however ineffectual) should always be taken seriously and advice sought.

Are sleeping tablets necessary?

Sleeping tablets are meant for short term use but often you will find that new residents may have been on these drugs long term. Discuss with the GP and the resident whether these drugs are still needed. Simple sleep hygiene advice (e.g. no caffeine after 8pm, a regular bedtime routine and not catnapping in the day) might be all you need.

Case History

On examination it was clear that Edith was depressed and needed treatment. It emerged that her daughter had noticed the depression many weeks earlier. She presumed the staff knew and so said nothing. The staff had not noticed so treatment started late, causing unnecessary stress to all concerned. Communication matters.

Know the signs of lithium toxicity (overdose)

If a resident is on lithium it is important that staff are aware of the signs of lithium overdose, which can be fatal. Signs include a sudden onset of reduced co-ordination, coarse tremor, confusion, drowsiness, and slurred speech. Lithium toxicity can be brought on by gastrointestinal upsets and dehydration. If you or your staff notice any of these signs seek an urgent medical review.

Does change in behaviour have a physical cause?

Whenever there is a change in the way a resident with mental health issues behaves always think whether it has a physical health cause. In particular, could the resident be in pain? Inadequately treated pain can severely impact mental health.

Implementing change

L ike it or not, care homes are subject to constant change; from new staff and residents through to changes in regulation or ownership, and developments in care. What sets a great care home manager above the rest is the ability to implement change and to look for continuous improvement. At Jewish Care, we talk passionately about change. We believe that times are changing and we need to change with them if we are to provide care services that meet the needs and aspirations of the community. Our ten top tips for implementing successful change are:

SIMON MORRIS
is chief executive Jewish Care, a leading health and social care provider. He has been working in social care for more than 30 years.

Know why change is necessary and create urgency for the change

Being able to explain the reason for change is essential. Without this you will fall at the first hurdle. Setting the scene and outlining a timeframe is key to ensuring success from the outset.

Don't try to do it alone

The best managers bring their team with them on their change journey. Implementing change alone is a recipe for failure. Start with identifying a team of movers and shakers who can help you deliver and get them on board first.

Create your vision

You know why the change is necessary and have your army of supporters. Bring the two together and create your vision for the future. Be realistic yet aspirational. The vision not only sells the change but, importantly, is the goal you are working towards.

Communicate the vision

Not just once but all the time. Consider how the change impacts on day-to-day life in the home and reinforce the need for change and the vision 'every day in every way'.

Remove the obstacles

There aren't always obstacles but more often than not there are. This can be systems or processes, or people. You need to decide how to manage those who can't back the vision.

Identify some short term wins

Change can take time. Any short term wins will help bring more people on board and create a greater momentum for the large scale change.

Don't declare a win too soon

Build on change, it's a process that won't happen overnight. Successful change needs to have real value to it, this takes time.

Ensure the change is embedded into the culture of your care home

This obviously depends on the nature of the change but generally successful change with value needs to be part of your care home and/or organisation's culture and vision for the future.

See change as part of continuous improvement, not a means to an end

This links into my point about not declaring a win too soon. Change isn't about developing a dusty report that then sits on a shelf, but about understanding its value and working towards a vision. This is the basis for ongoing developments and improvements. They often result in further change but no one ever gets it right first time.

Change is part and parcel of the role

This is something that you as a care home manager know well. If your ability to influence the type and speed of change at a wider organisational level is limited, you may want to consider that it is difficult to do good work in this type of environment.

"Change is the law of life and those who look only to the past or present are certain to miss the future."

—JOHN F. KENNEDY

12
End of life care

Palliative care: providing the very best

The only given for us all is that we will die. A good life deserves a good death and to achieve this we need to talk and make our wishes known to those we love and those who will care for us, our GP and other key people. Some of us will die unexpectedly, others will have life-limiting conditions, or may be older with dementia and access to good palliative care is so important wherever we live and whatever our condition. The National Council for Palliative Care and its Dying Matters coalition can help you with its good practice and user-friendly resources.

EVE RICHARDSON

is chief executive of the National Council for Palliative Care and the Dying Matters Coalition. The NCPC is an influential umbrella charity that promotes equity of access to good palliative care for all who need it, across all sectors. The Dying Matters coalition was set up to raise public awareness about dying, death and bereavement and has more than 30,000 members.

If I am no longer able to communicate easily

Please see my life story and plan – I carry it everywhere in my bag. Please read it and use it but I hope you know it already and that we have discussed my wishes.

Please consider my physical and practical needs

Do I have to lie in this position? I need the loo but can't reach the help button. I'm really thirsty but I cannot reach my drink. Even though I find it hard to speak, it doesn't mean I'm stupid.

Please consider my pain relief

I do want pain relief, especially at night, but I am on other tablets too so be aware of the mix. I might have dementia but it is my mouth that hurts. I might have toothache, and my food is hard to eat as swallowing is difficult.

Please consider my emotional needs

I never got round to saying goodbye to a few dear friends – please contact them. My life story tells you what I hate and what I love too. I feel really scared of what's going to happen – please talk to me first – not my family because they'll just worry.

Look after me and those I love with dignity and respect

Please try and make sure my loved ones are with me as much as they want to be. They can help with my care as they know what I want. I want to see my husband as I die and to hear him say how much he loves me.

What I would like to do before I die

I do hope my home has views of the sea. If not I would like to go to the sea to hear the waves and have an ice cream Ideally with my husband and/or with a carer who knows me and likes me.

Let me have music of my choice

I have a list of what I want when I am dying, as well as for my funeral. I want candlelight and incense if I die at night, and keep my mouth moist with good champagne.

Who's going to look after my dog?

My plan tells you about my dog's needs and where she likes to be walked. Please do not let her be alone, or run away. She is my constant friend.

I wish I'd updated my will

I wanted to leave my garden gnomes to another; more money to the person who has agreed to look after my animals and water my flowers. At least I made a will, so my loved ones are safe and not left with a mess to sort out.

My spiritual needs

I have set out my funeral wishes in my plan produced by Dying Matters, down to the last detail. Please use and read my wishes and spiritual needs and make sure my funeral is a celebration of my life.

"I have no doubt that this pre-death period is the most important and potentially the most fulfilling and the most inspirational time of my life. In this world, conventional time becomes meaningless. You map your course according to the co-ordinates of emotion and feelings, compassion and love."

– PHILIP GOULD, WHEN I DIE

Caring for a resident who is dying

RACHAEL STARKEY

has spent 23 years in the care sector. She is a qualified mental health nurse who was a ward sister at a local hospital prior to becoming a home manager seven years ago.

During the time a resident lives in our home we have the opportunity of carrying out many activities with them and their loved ones. If, for whatever reason, we do not completely carry out the task to perfection, we can apologise and repeat it. This is not so when caring for a resident who is dying. This is an aspect of our role that we "must" ensure is correct, as we will never be able to repeat it, no amount of apologising will ever be enough. Caring for a resident during their final journey is a privilege and an honour.

Knowing the person
An important part of all admissions is the prospect of our involvement with 'dying and death' despite our aim to promote 'living'. Staff members must be trained in this area so they are confident enough to approach this subject and able truly to get to know each person. Each person is unique.

Dignity
Each person has the right to pass with dignity, and to have their wishes and needs respected at all times. They are a person, a relative, a loved one. Do not just see them as a 'dying person'. They are alive until their final breath, and can usually hear all that you say.

Pain-free
As carers caring for someone taking their final path we must ensure that this course is taken painlessly. We must communicate with the full team of professionals ensuring that no distress or discomfort is felt. All pressure areas must be monitored, and oral care particularly carefully maintained.

Loved ones
We must ensure that we don't only care for our resident but also their loved ones and extended family. Families will have their own beliefs and customs; ensure that you listen to them. Those left behind must feel that they were involved in meeting their loved one's wishes.

Help staff to know what to do
Staff require support when caring for a dying resident. Some residents may become scared and agitated as they reach their final hours so staff members need to be able to recognise these symptoms, be aware of local policies in place in relation to palliative/end of life pathways, and know what to do.

Spirituality

The term "spirituality" doesn't just refer to religion; it is about so much more. True person-centred care takes account of what the person wishes for, not you or their next of kin. Ensure that the resident is listened to and all lasting wishes are upheld, even the occasional "bizarre" ones if possible!

Hospital or home

A resident's last place of comfort is very important; staff must be aware of everyone's wishes in relation to staying at home or in hospital, and that this is communicated to all. These procedures must be in place prior to a resident's dying to eliminate additional distress or confusion for all.

Communication

It's vital that staff are always truthful with the resident and their family, only making promises they know they are able to keep. The resident and family should be at the forefront of any decision-making and remain involved at all times. All actions offered, discussed or carried out must be documented in the resident's care plan.

'My mark'

Some people wish to "slip" away and are content to be an everlasting memory in our hearts. Others however may like a more lasting memorial in the home, which can be discussed with all. This is very often a comforting tribute to all who have known the person.

"What lies behind us and what lies before us are tiny matters compared to what lies within us."

– Henry S Haskins

Supporting relatives of a resident who is dying

GILLIAN CREASER

is a chaplain with MHA Group and considers it is a tremendous privilege to offer spiritual and pastoral support to residents and relatives as life draws to a close.

The death of a loved one is not always a tragedy, particularly following a long life, but it can be a time of profoundly deep emotion for relatives. Some long for death to come quickly for their nearest and dearest, others may be in denial that death is now inevitable, continuing to hope for recovery until the last breath. The most frequently asked question is probably 'When', and is impossible to answer – end of life care is not an exact science and people are all different. Honesty is important to avoid giving false hope or raising undue alarm.

Meeting them 'where they are'

It is important to allow relatives to express their feelings at this time. Families can display many different emotions as death approaches – shock, fear, sorrow, guilt, regret, disbelief, uncaring, pleasure, delight, humour. Try to be tactful and non-judgmental – you have no idea what has taken place previously in the relationship.

Check understanding

Death can be a 'taboo' subject. Sensitive questioning will verify relatives' awareness that the resident is dying. People may be reluctant to accept that death approaches, and euphemisms are unhelpful in aiding understanding. Personal wishes, cultural and faith matters concerning death should also be shared and discussed.

Symptoms of approaching death

Believing a loved one is hungry or thirsty causes distress. Explanation of why the body needs less fuel when 'closing down' is helpful. Information about other symptoms that may occur and the ready availability of drugs to relieve them also bring comfort to relatives, helping their understanding of what to expect.

Hearing continues to the end

Don't talk about an unresponsive resident as if they are not there, they may be listening! Behave as if they are wide awake. Encourage the relatives to talk to their loved one, familiar voices talking about shared memories will comfort the dying, letting them know they are not alone.

Can people choose when to die?

Collected experiences suggest some people wait a considerable time for an event or a particular visitor, while others may wait until the moment when, after days of vigil, relatives all go for a meal, to die quietly alone. Advising relatives beforehand can prevent feelings of disappointment or guilt.

Creature comforts

Sitting vigil with the dying is exhausting, yet there may be reluctance to leave the bedside. Offer to sit with their loved one while they take a needed break. Bring refreshments, reminding relatives to eat and drink; tell people where they can make drinks, smoke or sit quietly for a rest.

How to visit with the dying

Encourage visitors to talk, visiting family groups to chat to one another. A Bible or poetry book may give a lone visitor something to read aloud. Lead by example with physical contact, holding the resident's hand or stroking their face. Ask about favourite flowers, scents, music that could still bring pleasure during final hours.

Case History

His family journeyed with him during his last week – wife, children, grandchildren; they toasted him with wine, reminisced about family life, ate together, prayed, slept in his room or rested elsewhere, all gathered with him when he died peacefully. They were so grateful for those precious last days together.

Planning for after death

It may be possible for family to discuss funeral arrangements, music or readings, with the resident – one of our families wrote their Father's Eulogy which he then added to and edited, and his daughters took solace from knowing that his funeral service was exactly as he wished.

Time

Be available to support the family but without intruding – you will sense if they wish to be alone with their loved one. After death and doctor's certification the family may wish to spend time with the deceased before re-engaging with the outside world following what may have been an intensely emotional period.

Listen

Family members often experience feelings of guilt about past events or worry that they have not done enough for their loved one before or after death. Vocalising this, often to a non-family member such as a chaplain, and reassurance will help assuage these feelings. Be prepared to listen and comfort.

Supporting staff who are working with a resident who is dying

REV DR KEITH ALBANS *has been director of chaplaincy and spirituality at MHA since 2001. Keith has taken a lead role in changing culture by devising and delivering staff training in end of life care.*

A surprising number of managers never ask potential care staff at interview their feelings about dealing with dying residents or with their bodies after death. In today's death denying culture few of us have to handle death on a regular basis, so offering staff support in this essential element of their job is vital. Likewise, as most staff will learn what to do around a resident's death from colleagues, it is important to ensure that a culture of openness is developed, where staff can share concerns and insights so that the best end of life care can be offered.

Don't make assumptions

Knowing your staff, their experience or lack of it, their natural capabilities and the aspects of work they struggle with is vital, particularly in end of life care. But each resident and each death is unique, so never assume that a staff member, however experienced, will just cope.

Develop your mentors

The ability to inspire confidence in inexperienced care staff is invaluable. Once you have established good protocols in the home, and set out a culture of openness to be developed, identify one or two members of the care team who can model good practice to colleagues, and use them wisely.

Make use of the learning opportunities

With new care staff joining the team, particularly in homes where residents' deaths are less frequent, ensure that they are involved in some part of the final days when a resident is dying, so that with support from the mentor they can be helped to address any fears or concerns.

Be prepared

The 'Final Wishes' in a resident's care plan were completed for a reason – ensure care staff are familiar with its contents and, if it has particularly specific requests, that they have the resources to meet them. Also ensure that they can access the default resources for a peaceful 'departure lounge'.

Key worker's role is key

In terms both of knowledge about a resident, and potentially having a relationship with their relatives, the resident's key-worker needs to be at the heart of offering care and support as death approaches. Shift patterns may need tweaking and individuals may be given the choice to come in when off-shift.

Death is not the end of caring

Preparing the body after death is a caring act – it's why we speak to them while we do it! Particularly when relatives have not been present, preparing the room and presenting the body well will help them begin the grieving process well, and will remain in their memory for ages.

Saying goodbye

Staff are helped if given the opportunity to say their goodbyes, either as a resident is dying or afterwards before their body leaves the home. Involving other residents, if they wish to be, in this works towards an open culture and reassures other residents that they will not simply 'disappear'.

Case History

She was worried the manager would criticise her for lying down next to a dying resident. "I remember them saying that hearing was the last sense to go. She was deaf so I didn't want to shout as she died. So I spoke gently in her ear that we loved her."

Gone but not forgotten

Creating opportunities for the community to speak about and remember the resident who has died can help everyone. Sharing the things about them we liked as well as things which annoyed us can provoke a sense of thankfulness that we knew them and a feeling of a job well done.

Time out

Caring for a dying resident, before and after death, can be emotionally draining for staff. Senior staff need to be aware and ensure that some 'time out' is allowed before another caring task is undertaken. Individuals' needs vary, but the opportunity to unwind and refocus will help reduce workplace stress.

How was it for you?

Reviewing the staff team's experiences and feelings following a resident's death, whether in a team meeting or in a one-to-one, will give opportunities for feedback to be given, lessons to be learned and plans for the future to be made. There may also be feedback to be shared with external professionals.

Thoughts about death and bereavement

JEREMY NIXEY
was a Benedictine monk and then priest until he met his wife. Jeremy set up ten Welsh Housing Associations then a 75 care home staff-owned business.

Faced with death it helps if we speak freely of our sadness and grief: our loss is witness to the love we had. But having grieved for due time, life goes on and we must start again. Someone's life is not gone; it lives on in those to whom they gave life, love and laughter.

Speak it out

It is because we loved them that we miss them; would we have had it any other way? We can help by remembering this and speaking it out.

We carry them with us

Those we love change us and so become a part of us. In this way they are not utterly gone but remain with us. We carry our parents inside us and our partners too.

Take time to grieve

Yet we must give in to grief for a while. We need to cry out and express our pain and loss – if we don't let it out it can burn on inside us, even for years.

Talk to the bereaved

Talk to the bereaved of your memories of the one they loved and have lost. They want to hear them and need to talk and hear talk of their loved one. They are hungry for your memories. Don't leave them in a circle of silence – speak of and celebrate the one they loved.

A reason for suffering?

Did they need to suffer so? For some religious faiths there is a meaning and purpose in suffering. For those outside a religious tradition few have come up with an answer to this question. But we can all see that some do suffer terribly and there is no obvious reason why they drew this bad card out of life's pack any more than any of us earned the right to be alive in the first place.

What we have given is what counts

What was the point of it all? "In the evening of our life all that will matter is how we have loved." These words are attributed to Saint John who is described in the Bible as "the disciple whom Jesus loved". The love and laughter that we have given others is the real measure of our life's achievement and it will be for this that people remember and think of us with pleasure.

Life is for the living

People who are fortunate enough to find another great love after a great loss can feel they are betraying their loved one. But they are not: they would not be in this new relationship if their earlier loved one was there. Life is for the living and the right response is to seize life and love when and where we can.

Don't be a misery-guts

Life doesn't only happen to you – you need to go and find love and laughter again. The mood you choose to be in day after day will be how you see the world – and how the world will see you. Not for long will the world tolerate a misery-guts: it will prefer to move on to talk to and be with others who are more fun to be with.

"At the end all shall be well and all manner of things shall be well."

– ONE OF THE MOST QUOTED WRITINGS OF MOTHER JULIAN OF NORWICH, A WIDELY KNOWN AND RESPECTED MYSTIC IN MEDIAEVAL ENGLAND WHO LIVED AS A HERMIT NEXT TO THE CATHEDRAL AT NORWICH.

Live life now

We only live today; yesterday is gone and tomorrow is not yet. Live and love now – you may not have tomorrow.

Sometime silence is better than words

To be alone with oneself and our grief is right and necessary at times. It can also be helpful just to be silently with the one who is grieving.

13
Reflections

Reflections on the care sector after many years with Care Forum Wales

MARIO KREFT MBE

is a founder of Care Forum Wales which was a founder of the Five Nations group. Mario is also owner of Pendine Park Care Organisation.

I came to social care by accident because of personal circumstances – my beloved grandmother had dementia and needed care and support. My wife and I couldn't find anywhere suitable so we set up our own care home. This personal experience was the foundation of the values that guide me still. My philosophy is to provide a social care service that you would want for a loved one, which promotes independence and where people are treated with dignity and respect. We are passionate about giving people the best possible care in a homely environment.

A clear vision

Make sure you have a clear purpose and vision and constantly work towards achieving it. This must be the starting point for everyone.

It's about people

Person-centred care and relationship-centred care are popular buzz words, but we must always remember we are talking about people. Social care is about putting people at the heart of everything we do.

Staff development

A universal commitment to personal and professional development of staff is vital. The people who work for you are your biggest asset. To provide the very best service for an individual can only be done by having a highly motivated, dedicated, well-trained team of people.

Enriching lives

Enriching people's lives is our guiding principle. We must improve the quality of life of our residents, making every moment matter. Make sure people have a purpose in life and as far as they are able, can do as they choose.

Embrace the arts

The arts enrich our lives. We took 100 members of our team to see the film *Quartet* which is set in a residential home for musicians. We turned the visit into a training workshop which emphasised what the arts can do to lift people's spirits. The reaction of the staff was incredible.

Paperwork doesn't guarantee quality

The social care sector is heavily regulated and rightly so. We must not rely solely on paperwork as a measure of quality. I believe if you put quality standards into values and cultures, this makes them real and they will be delivered every day.

Influential representation

I can't emphasise enough the importance of clear and influential representation for the sector. Care Forum Wales, celebrating its 20th anniversary this year, provides a single voice for the sector in Wales. Scotland also benefits from a single voice and in England the coming together of the English Community Care Association and the National Care Association to create a new organisation called Care England is welcome.

"A small body of determined spirits fired by an unquenchable faith in their mission can alter the course of history."

– Mahatma Gandhi

Sharing best practice

You can be in competition and still work collaboratively. Partnership is the key to our future success. Competitors should work together for the greater good, sharing best practice and learning wherever possible.

Business viability

Your business model needs to be sustainable. Over the last couple of decades more and more of social care has been placed in the independent sector. It is essential that regulated settings are viable and all stakeholders understand how viability transfers into high standards.

Join an association

Wherever you are, I would strongly recommend you join a *bona fide* representative organisation that has quality at its heart and can provide a voice that health boards and government at local and national levels listen to. As a sector, we need to be greater than the sum of our individual parts.

Reflections on the care sector after many years with ECCA

Prof. Martin Green obe

is chief executive of ECCA, chair of ILC-UK, a Trustee of National Aids Trust, a Dignity Commissioner and Independent Sector Dementia Champion for the DH. .In 2013 he was appointed Visiting Professor of Social Care to Bucks New University.

The care sector is going through unprecedented change. Not only do we have to face the enormous challenges of government funding cuts, but we are also grappling with increasing need, a population whose expectations are rising, and a media that only wants to expose and sensationalise, rather than present a balanced picture.

We work in a sector able to withstand pressure

This would seem like the worst moment to be involved in the health and social care system and for many it will be the tipping point that will motivate them to leave the sector, or change their career. However, we are working in a sector that is used to pressure, and is filled with people who are committed to improving care and supporting people in need.

What we desperately need is stability

One thing that is incredibly unhelpful, and is responsible for the storm we are weathering, is the constant politicisation of health and social care, which seems to instil in every government that comes to power, the conviction that the path to improvements lies in structural change. What health and social care desperately needs is some stability in its structure and a focus on culture change.

Culture and values define whether the sector can deliver

What politicians seem incapable of understanding, is that structures in themselves do not define how an organisation is run. Far more important is getting the culture right and ensuring that all those people who work in the system share its vision and values, and are committed to ensuring high quality outcomes for those who use the services.

You have to be accountable for your actions and practice

We need people to understand that structures are there to support them, but ultimately they are responsible for what they do and how they interact with their service users. It is vitally important that we reconnect people with the accountability they must have for their own work.

Perform and deliver or expect to be fired

We need to performance-manage people so that they either deliver a high quality outcome or they leave. The public sector has the most appalling record on performance management with people not able to do their job staying in post because the system lacks the guts to tell them that they need to either shape-up and deliver, or get out.

Let's get real with health and social care

The disproportionate allocation of resources between health and social care is a throwback to a simplistic 1948 scenario where people were diagnosed, treated and then cured. In the 21st-century people are diagnosed and treated, but ultimately have to manage living with a long-term condition because no cure is available. This reality should mean resources are allocated more equally between health and social care.

Our vision should be long-term and strategic

Modern horizons seem to last only from one election to the next. If we are going to deliver the 21st-century service that is able to plan into the long-term, we have got to get out of political timescales, and move towards a much more strategic and long-term view.

Case History

PJ Care has a fantastic integrated health and social care facility in Peterborough, which has the capacity to deliver both medical and social care outcomes. The difficulty has been the reluctance of local commissioners to engage with this service, and this is due to the fact that in-house provision in that area is not as good, and is more expensive. In many ways, PJ Care has exposed this and this is uncomfortable for health and social care commissioners, who should de-commission their own services, as well as commission new ones.

Cut loose from political control

I would like to see the NHS and social care taken out of the control of both national and local politicians, and turned over, as the Bank of England was, to independent people committed to a long-term and sustainable future.

Innovative, appropriate services are what we need

What is certain, as we face the realities of demographic change, is that we not only need to plan our current services better, but we also need to have a strategy to dismantle some of the inappropriate and unnecessary provision that exists, and to move our resources to new and innovative services.

Unpopular but necessary

The final thing that needs to happen is going to be very unpopular. We need to have an adult dialogue with citizens about what health services are here to do and what responsibilities all people have for their own lives. The future will be difficult and it will require change from everyone. Only by working together and reaffirming an agreed vision for health and social care services do we stand any chance of responding to the needs that will confront us in the coming decades.

Reflections on the care sector after many years with the National Care Association

I began working for National Care Association in 1987 following the sale of the two care homes I owned. The move from long term care being provided by local authorities and the NHS to smaller private and not-for-profit organisations has, I believe, led to the biggest conundrum of all – how can huge organisations such as local authorities and health authorities ever understand the challenges facing a small care home and, of course, vice-versa. As we move ever closer to integrated health and social care the Department of Health perhaps needs to consider how this particular barrier is to be broken down.

SHEILA SCOTT OBE

is a nurse by profession and has worked in social care for 35 years first as a provider and for the last 25 years representing the National Care Association.

Investment in the workforce...

There has been a real investment by government and providers in the workforce and this has undoubtedly had an impact on the quality of care provided. The investment has been across the workforce, from managers to care workers to other staff such as cooks and chefs.

... but little progress in professionalisation

It has been a real disappointment that little progress has been made in the professionalisation of the social care workforce despite the millions of pounds that I suspect were invested in this aspect of the work of the General Social Care Council.

Quality of life

There is a great deal of discussion about quality in social care and of course quality of care and quality of life are at the heart of everything we do. It is key to the provision of an holistic service for all that commissioners recognise that quality of life is as essential to the wellbeing of people receiving care as is the quality of care.

A national regulator

Campaigning for a national independent regulator of services has been a cornerstone of the work of the National Care Association and we are delighted that that was finally achieved in 2002. There have been too many changes since then and it is essential that the Care Quality Commission now ups their game to meet the expectations of the public and the sector.

Recruitment checks

The introduction of the Criminal Record Bureau and now the Disclosure and Barring Service was an important step forward for the sector allowing them to have much more confidence in their recruiting processes.

Mental capacity legislation

The Mental Capacity Act 2005 bought a similar reassurance to the sector. This legal framework to protect the rights of people who may lack capacity provides a framework for care staff to operate in, and as a consequence confidence has increased among social care staff.

A common language

We need to address the language barrier I have always believed exists between local authorities and the independent care sector. For instance, if you take a simple word like 'personalisation' I so often find that the two parties mean something similar but not the same!

"If there is to be a real partnership between all the stakeholders working in social care then all stakeholders must recognise the experience and expertise of providers and managers in the private sector."

Funding shortfall

Funding has been a challenge for social care since 1993 at least but it has got much worse in the last few years. There has been an absolute failure by government, both national and local, to acknowledge the shortfall. In my opinion this is by far and away the biggest threat to social care provision that I have seen in the last 25 years.

Negative media coverage

A recent trend by national government has been to "knee jerk" react to media comments about the sector when something goes wrong in an individual provision. It is essential to remember that the vast majority of social care providers are responsible organisations who want the very best for the people they care for.

Care England

During the last ten years I never thought that I would see the day when National Care Association would join with English Community Care Association but, from 1st January 2014, Care England is the result. This is good news for the sector.

Reflections on the care sector

It has been a privilege to have spent the whole of my working life in the care sector. I have worked at the front end of care and support, managed care services at middle and senior management levels, taught and researched and represented. Relationship-centred care has rightly come to define best practice. Those relationships – many and varied – are what make working in the care sector such a joy. Looking back I am reminded that time goes by very quickly (and it seems to speed up!) so we shouldn't settle for anything less than the best we can manage . . . and never, ever say 'I'm just a carer'!

DES KELLY OBE

is executive director of the National Care Forum. He was a member of the Wagner Committee Residential Care: A Positive Choice (1988) which led to a lifelong quest to improve the quality of care services.

Ideas have to have their time

An understanding of what happened before is generally helpful, as is being able to take a long-term view. You might have to try, and try, and try again to get an idea to take root.

Values are fundamental

The way we relate to people is the essence of care and it is vital that the way we work is informed by values that support such characteristics as choice and control for individuals, dignity and respect, the promotion of individuality, diversity and interdependency.

Quality is a continuing quest

Notions of quality evolve and develop. Striving for excellence is of course essential but remember that perfection is quite often elusive.

Master the management of change

Successful change doesn't just happen. Change demands that we question what we do and why . . . all the time. Change is what effective managers do well.

Information is education

More information and better understanding by the public of care and support services is the best form of quality assurance and quality control. More and better information will change services.

Learning and practice

We never stop learning and should never stop practising. Use training as a reminder of the importance of reflecting on what you do. Learning, training and development, supervision and support are seamless treads that run through best practice.

Pay attention to job satisfaction

It is essential that people know they are valued in the workplace. Be generous in giving positive feedback and praise. Pride, enthusiasm and passion may not be seen in management texts but in my experience are always present in the best services.

Respect the innovators

Innovators question the established order and they are prepared to take risks. Both of these are necessary and have a place in improving the quality of care provision. However inspiration is not sufficient for good leadership.

A mixed economy enhances choice

The not-for-profit model of care provision offers a distinctive contribution in the care sector. It is much more prevalent in other parts of the world than it is in the UK.

Value collaboration

Effective partnership working brings benefits greater than the sum of the parts. Working to build consensus for the 'greater good' may mean that vested interests and egos have to be set aside.

"When people not used to speaking are heard by people not used to listening, then real change can be made."

– John O'Brien

Reflections of the care sector after many years with the RNHA

FRANK URSELL

has been chief executive of the Registered Nursing Home Association since 1991, and a nursing home owner since 1983. Frank combines pragmatism with experience in representing owners of nursing homes.

As the oldest of the care home associations, the Registered Nursing Home Association (RNHA) was formed in 1968 by a group of nursing home owners and matrons who regularly met in Exeter to discuss standards of care in nursing homes and the training of staff, and these objectives continue to this day. The original philosophies of representing owners of nursing homes and championing the special value which nurses bring to the care of older people, combined with the belief in the best training and education of nursing home staff, remain at the forefront to this day of all that the association stands for.

Our offices over the years
Our first offices were in the garage of our general secretary, Stanley Davies, in Finchley, London. As the association grew more space was needed and we moved across London to Portland Place. 1986 saw a move to rented offices in Birmingham and in 2006 we purchased our current offices in Kings Norton, Birmingham.

Reflections lead to two themes emerging
Looking back over my 30 years as a nursing home owner it is most evident that there have been two themes which most impact on care homes; regulation and the State funding of patients. These two themes continue to dominate, while the care of patients is often subsumed by the actions determined by these themes.

First of the legal milestones in regulation
The introduction of the Registered Homes Act in 1984 was the first to attempt to specify what was expected of both care home owners (Part 1) and nursing home owners (Part 2). The challenges which followed led to the association appointing a legal panel of solicitors to support members where necessary.

National regulators and National Minimum Standards
The next major event affecting the regulation of care homes came with the Care Standards Act 2000 which introduced the National Care Standards Commission and, for the first time, National Minimum Standards. While there was little controversy with most of the new standards, rooms size and singles *v* double rooms dominated the debate.

Changes to regulators
NCSC only lasted 17 days before their successor, the Commission for Social Care Inspection (CSCI) was announced. CSCI lasted longer, but was replaced in 2010 by the Care Quality Commission in order to merge the NHS and Adult Social Care and introduce new joint, standards. For many of us the jury is still out as to the efficacy of this move.

Introduction of Income Support

In the early 1980s, for the first time, people who were unable to pay for care in a care home could get a fixed amount of income support to pay for that care. This led to an expansion in the number of care homes, especially nursing homes, and was considered by most as a period when fees best met the needs of residents and patients.

Local authority funded care

Probably the greatest impact over the past 30 years has been the move, in 1993, from the Income Support right of an individual to a payment to meet care home fees, to the capped assessment process now controlled by local authorities. The resulting 'race to the bottom' in fees has done nothing for the quality of care.

"Reflecting on the outcomes over the last 30 years, the question comes to mind as to whether or not it is successive governments' policy to fund care for our older people by the least well paid and least well qualified workforce. Because this is precisely what their funding policy has achieved over this period of time."

The earliest legal challenge, circa 1980

Over the years there have been a number of significant legal challenges by the RNHA which have changed the face of care. Our first real success was against the Rate Relief Act, using our general secretary, Paddy Carr, as one of the test cases, which resulted in care homes not having to pay rates.

Judicial Reviews

RNHA still fights legal battles on behalf of members, but there is nothing comforting in having to divert money, which is better spent on care, to fighting Judicial Reviews against local authorities on the level of fees paid. That this has become necessary is perhaps, the saddest reflection of all.

The continuing value of nurses

Over the years we have seen a constant drive for a single care home, eventually introduced by the Care Standards Act 2000. The argument has always been where the dividing line is drawn. In reality the difference is understood and it only becomes a problem when it determines the fees to be paid. Money v care still rules!

Reflections on social care in a Scottish context

RANALD MAIR

is chief executive of Scottish Care. He has worked in social care and social work for more than 40 years. He remains married to a very tolerant wife and has two allegedly grown-up sons.

Is there something distinctive about the Scottish system? Is there a care tartan that differentiates us from the delivery of care down south? – "down south" of course being anywhere below Gretna on a map of the British Isles!

Size matters

I suppose the first thing to admit is that size does matter, or in our case the lack of it. Being a country half the size of Greater London allows an immediacy of interaction between the different levels of government, local agencies, the care sector and the public. This has the positive advantage of allowing some matters to be progressed more quickly and making dialogue between the relevant parties easier to manage.

Mole-hills into mountains

However, there is also the clear challenge that issues, such as failures of care, which might in other contexts simply be seen as local, become matters of national significance.

Free personal care?

Like parts of England, Wales and Northern Ireland, Scotland prides itself in having a deep-rooted culture of social justice, community participation, and care for vulnerable and disadvantaged groups. This does manifest itself in some of the distinctive elements of the Scottish system, such as free personal and nursing care (which doesn't actually mean free care, but would take too long to explain!).

Inherent suspicion

The values above lead to other challenges; the emphasis on public provision, and an inherent suspicion of the independent sector.

Homecare

Homecare in particular is almost a battle ground between the drive by councils to maintain higher cost in-house services and the move towards externally purchased homecare. The overall market share between in-house and external independent provision across the country is around 50-50, but with in-house provision costing up to twice as much.

Care homes

The care home sector is more in line with other parts of the UK, with councils having around 19% of the provision in-house, at a significantly higher cost compared to publicly purchased care.

Values must be challenged

Like elsewhere, we still have to win the battle over the funding of care for older people. Despite the rhetoric, you could be forgiven for thinking there was underlying ageism in social care provision, certainly in the allocation of resources: average children's home placement – £2,500 per week, average older person's placement – £600. Quite rightly as a society we want to provide positive life-enhancing care for young people, but we seem prepared to settle for warehousing when it comes to those approaching end of life. Providers and provider organisations have to take on a campaigning and advocacy role on behalf service users, and not just accept the prevailing limits to the care they provide.

Regulation and inspection

Regulation and inspection of care in Scotland lies with the Care Inspectorate, and services continue to be inspected at least once per year and graded on 4 key themes: quality of environment, quality of management and leadership, quality of staffing and quality of care and support. However, the danger is that inspection becomes a mechanistic, box-ticking exercise. Quality requires a collective commitment to excellence, not just the attempt to eradicate poor performance.

"To be like a little inn which rejects no one who is in need but which is afterwards forgotten or ridiculed! To possess no advantage – but to give away, to give back, to communicate, to grow poorer! To be able to be humble, so as to be accessible to many and humiliating to none! That would be a reason for a long life."

– Nietzsche

The right people in the right places

Against all the challenges: finance, demography, public scrutiny, higher levels of dependency and complexity of need, how do we make the system work? More than anything else, it means getting the right people into the care sector, at all levels, and across all agencies.

Vocation, vocation, vocation

Care is not just a job, a profession or a business, it remains a vocation. It has to be what gets you out of bed in the morning, and delays you getting to bed at night. It is an undertaking and commitment about which there can be no compromise. Either do it right or don't do it at all. In this regard, the care sector in Scotland is no different from anywhere else.